A GAME OF SOLDIERS

JAN NEEDLE

Notes and Extension Work
Vivien Gardner

Additional Material
Stephen Cockett

Series Consultant
Cecily O'Neill

Collins Educational
An Imprint of HarperCollins*Publishers*

www.**Collins**Education.com
On-line Support for Schools and Colleges

First published 1985 by Collins Educational, London and Glasgow.
Reprinted 1985, 1986, 1987, 1988, 1989, 1990, 1995, 1997, 1998,
2000, 2001

ISBN 00 330231 8

Acknowledgements

The following permissions to reproduce material
are gratefully acknowledged: *Daily Mail*, page 47;
Daily Mirror, pages 48, 61; *Daily Express*, page 49;
A Message from the Falklands – the letters of
David Tinker, RN, compiled by Hugh Tinker
(Junction Books), pages 50, 51; Guillermo Gil and
The Guardian, pages 55, 56; *The Guardian*,
page 60; IPC Magazines Ltd, extracts from *Tammy*
and *Battle Action Force*, pages 66-69.

Design by The Pinpoint Design Company

Typeset by Hope Services, Abingdon.
Printed and bound in China

INTRODUCTION

When I was asked in the late summer of 1982 to write a
three-part television play for Thames Television's programme
'Middle English', the Falklands Crisis seemed an obvious
choice of subject. The active, violent part of the conflict was
over, but the underlying problem looked as insoluble as ever.
Nearly a thousand Britons and Argentinians were dead; the
occupation of the islands had ended, and both sides still
insisted that they were the rightful 'sovereigns'. At the time
of writing this, nearly two years later, there has still been no
formal recognition by Argentina that the hostilities are over
and the question of sovereignty is still in the air. The problem
will not go away.

Despite the fantastically complicated legal and historical
situation, the conflict was seen by the respective countries as
very simplistic and clear-cut at the time. To the British it was
a matter of the invasion of a peaceful island community by a
foreign force — a clearly illegal act. To the Argentinians it
was a matter of resolving at one stroke a question to which no
amount of talking had ever brought a solution.

A wave of indignation swept over Britain at the news of the
invasion, which was mirrored in Argentina when the British
despatched the Task Force (the 'pirate fleet' as it was known
there) to liberate the islands.

My idea in writing the play was simple. War has always
looked glamorous from afar, because, among other reasons, it
is inevitably perceived in terms of right and wrong. By
writing a story in which three children meet a fourth person
only a very few years older than themselves who they will
inevitably come to understand in human terms rather than in
terms of propaganda or simplistic moral labelling, I hoped I
could convey an awareness of the complexity, and the sheer

lack of glamour, behind the surface. The children move from a sense of outrage (received largely from their elders) at the fact of the invasion, through a contempt for all their enemies as human beings, to an awareness that something terrible is happening to everybody involved. The Argentinian soldier, let us say, suffers a similar process of enlightenment: a country boy, a proud conscript into a cause to restore his nation's honour, a freezing, lost, hungry casualty of war, a sacrifice.

The reaction to the play was enormous and very heartening. I was inundated with letters, projects and poems which sprang from the event. One question recurred again and again in the letters, however — what *exactly* happened to the Argentinian soldier in the end? It is not, I'm afraid, a question that can easily be answered.

The reasons why the play ends as it does are not simple, but there are two elements which should be touched upon. The first is to do with a necessary ambiguity, and the second concerns the way in which people respond to situations. Firstly, I wanted to allow each viewer to bring his or her mind to bear on the possibilities inherent in the ending. Does the Conscript die? If so, by whose hand, his own or the soldiers'? If he is killed, why? Is it, or can it be, justified? And if he does die, are the children in any way to blame? Working back from the ambiguity of the ending is the ambiguity inherent in the personalities and attitudes of the children from the moment they find the wounded Conscript. Just how far, and for how long, does Michael believe his plan to kill the Conscript is justified and/or possible? Why does Sarah swear to join in the murder? What does Thomas think — would he do it/not do it/do anything his elders suggested? Most importantly, how are all three of them changed by the experience?

One of the reactions to the play is, I think, worth quoting at length. It is from a report compiled by Anne Suffolk, Education Officer for Central Independent Television, and refers to a rural middle school with a socially mixed catchment area.

She writes:

'The two teachers concerned were horrified at the effect the Falklands story had on their class . . . when they saw the final episode with them.

The boys in the class were all for shooting the soldier, he

was an enemy, kill before you get killed, the Argentinians are the scum of the earth and he deserved it, etc., etc. There followed a very traumatic half hour as they let them talk it out, desire for violence and revenge emerged and a stream of racist invective followed, which led also onto unemployment, and a line in politics far to the right of Margaret Thatcher. At first the teachers thought it was macho bravado but realised that they had lifted a stone and been given an insight into what some of their local community really thought, not only about war and peace, but about a whole host of issues of deep social concern. Some of the girls in the class had cried at the ending and more cried when they tried to argue with the boys and got shouted down.

The film was discussed with the Head and as a result the school reappraised what it was doing in personal and moral education. It was particularly upsetting for them as theirs is a church school and they felt satisfied that they were instilling values of compassion and respect for others etc., but clearly had failed where some of the boys in the group were concerned. Ten days of discussion on the film with the two classes followed. . . .

No parent complained although the teachers and the Head felt that they would defend the film if one did. . . It was far better that these thoughts and feelings were out in the open and talked out with responsible adults . . . they considered the issues raised by it were too important to ignore.'

As I said at the beginning of this introduction, the violent phase of the Falklands Crisis was short-lived, and has been long over. But it was an extraordinary event, and is likely to remain a problematical issue for many years to come. I hope this text, and the notes and materials that follow it, help stimulate analysis of a tragic, important, and complicated phenomenon.

J.N.
September 1984

A Game of Soldiers was originally broadcast in three weekly episodes — hence the 'cliff-hanging' endings to certain scenes. The twelve scenes do run on, however, and can be read or performed as a single play.

There are, of course, many ways of tackling a dramatic text besides reading it or acting it out in its entirety. Not only could certain scenes be isolated for work by individuals or groups, but many of the scenes invite further exploration through improvisation or written work. Extensive suggestions for this and other follow-up work are included after the play-text itself.

V.G.
September 1984

CONTENTS

THE CHARACTERS

MICHAEL   He is twelve or thirteeen, wearing jeans, rubber boots, camouflage jacket and a bush hat. He has a small clasp knife that he plays with a lot.

SARAH   She is slightly older than Michael and wears an ordinary anorak, jeans, rubber boots and a scarf.

THOMAS   About eight, dressed in boots, jeans, anorak and woolly hat. Frequently the butt of Michael's sarcasm because he is so young. Sarah tries to protect him for the same reason.

THE SOLDIER   Aged sixteen to seventeen, injured and dirty. He is dressed in shabby military gear and carries a self-loading rifle.

A GAME OF SOLDIERS

SCENE ONE

The children are in their seaside den. It is an open hollow in the sand dunes overlooking the South Atlantic, and has a couple of boxes to sit on, maybe covered with cloth. There is also an old military radio-telephone set, with dials and a winding handle — **Michael's** *pride and joy. It is nearly winter, but sunny, and they are dressed up well against the cold.* **Sarah** *has some home-made toffee in a sheet of paper which she is handing round.*

THOMAS   You're lucky you are, Sarah. I wish my Mum made stuff like this.

MICHAEL   Your Mum would kill you if she saw you eating it. *Nasty grown-up voice*   Thomas Wyatt! How dare you! That rubbish will rot your little toothypegs!

SARAH   *to get* **Michael** *off* **Thomas's** *back*   She says we need it more now . . . now we've been invaded. She says toffee's what keeps you going.

THOMAS   What's she mean by that, though?

SARAH   Don't know really. I think it's because she remembers England, after the last one. They had rationing. You couldn't get sweets at all. You couldn't even get sugar to make toffee with. So she says we've got to have it now. Principle.

MICHAEL   Your Mum's as daft as you are, Sarah. Nutty.

SARAH   *offering paper of toffee to* **Thomas**   You don't have to eat it. Thomas and me'll be quite happy without your big gob at the trough.

1

MICHAEL Only joking, Sarah. I think your Mum's fantastic. Just like you!

SARAH Yuk! Here, have some. Stick your jaws together, quick!

They chew.

THOMAS Did you hear the firing last night? It woke me up.

MICHAEL I bet it did. I bet you nearly wet yourself. Did you call out for your Mummy?

SARAH I did. I got in bed with mine. It didn't half sound close, I was petrified.

MICHAEL I didn't hear a thing. I slept like a log. I bet it wasn't that close, anyway.

THOMAS You're wrong then, Cleverdick. My Dad says it's very close now and he said it's getting closer all the time. He said he was in two minds if I was to come out to play or not, he said it might be dangerous.

MICHAEL Yah, dangerous! He's wet, your Dad is. My old man could hardly wait to get me out of the house. He gets really fed up with me, now we can't go to school any more.

SARAH Pity the poor teachers. **They** put up with you! They deserve a medal, my Mum reckons. It's funny though, when you think about it, how everything's changed. I mean, here we are in our den, just as if nothing's happened, and we're at war. Somewhere out there there's ships, and submarines, and planes. And there's soldiers everywhere, crawling about with guns. It seems ridiculous.

MICHAEL You wouldn't think so if you met one face to face. You'd run a mile.

SARAH Fat chance of that though, isn't there? It's other people who always get the fun.

THOMAS They're despoilers, anyway. Evil despoilers.

MICHAEL Despoilers!? That's a big word for a little twit. What does it mean?

THOMAS Well I. . . Well, I think that's what Dad said. He said they're invaders, and despoilers, and rapists and that. Beasts.

MICHAEL Despoilers! Rapists! They're soldiers, that's what they are. The enemy. And they'll be driven into the sea. Or have their throats cut if the Gurkhas get them. They've had it. They're all dead men. They haven't got a chance.

They chew.

SARAH Thomas is lucky in one way though, Michael. You are though, Tom. Even if your parents are strict at least they tell you things. When I got in bed with mine last night, they just said not to worry, but they wouldn't say what about. They say it's mostly rumour, what we hear, and we shouldn't bother with it.

THOMAS I listened at the bedroom door. I heard them talking.

MICHAEL What? In the middle of the night?

THOMAS Yeah. I got up when I heard the guns. But I couldn't go in their room. It's not allowed. I heard them talking.

SARAH What did they say?

THOMAS My Dad said there'd been some of them about. Young ones. Cons. . . Cons . . . something.

MICHAEL Conscripts, I bet.

THOMAS Yeah, that's right, conscripts. What does that mean, Michael.

MICHAEL *proudly* It means they're not in voluntary. It means they've been forced to fight. Not like the Brits. **They're** fantastic. Professionals. **Real** soldiers.

SARAH Yes, don't go on and on. Carry on, Thomas. What else?

THOMAS He said some of these cons-things had got split up from their army. He said some of them had been found hiding, over Foster's Landing way. He said the farmers had found them, hiding in the straw.

MICHAEL Yeah. That's where that Mr Gregory lives. He drinks. He's a villain, my Mum says, a hothead. There's a group of them.

SARAH What happened to them, then? These soldiers?

THOMAS My Dad said . . . he said . . . he said they killed

3

them. Mr Gregory and the other . . . young-bloods. He said they banded them up. And killed them.

SARAH *horrified* I don't believe that! That's a great big story, Thomas Wyatt!

MICHAEL *unsure* Oh come on Sarah, they **are** the enemy.

SARAH It's a lie. You made it up.

THOMAS No . . . I. No. I think I. . . .

SARAH Yah! Think! It's a story you've made up.

THOMAS No, honestly.

MICHAEL *disgusted* You're a little weed you are, Thomas. I don't know why we play with you. You're a rotten little weed.

Thomas *stands up.*

THOMAS Well it's true, that's all. I'm **not** a liar! I **didn't** make it up! It's true! I'm going.

He rushes out of the shelter, and runs off.

SARAH *calls* Thomas! Tommy! Come back. *To* **Michael** You rotten pig, Michael. He's only a little boy.

She runs out after him. **Michael** *watches them go, then sits facing the bush radio. He winds the handle.*

MICHAEL Patrol to base. Patrol to base. Enemy pesonnel in area. Enemy personnel in area. What are your orders? Over.

He listens intently, moving his lips.

MICHAEL Patrol to base. Patrol to base. I read you loud and clear. Search and destroy. I repeat, search and destroy. Roger and out.

He takes out his penknife, opens it, and stalks out.

SCENE TWO

Thomas *and* **Sarah** *are sitting on a rock overlooking the sea.* **Sarah's** *arm is around* **Thomas's** *shoulder. He has been crying.*

4

THOMAS Why does he get at me all the time, though, Sarah? I haven't done anything different. Michael always gets at me now, and I'm **not** a weed. Not any more than I always was, anyway.

SARAH Don't worry about it, Thomas. He's gone a bit nutty since this lot started, that's all. He loves it. He thinks he's a real soldier, like a grown-up.

THOMAS But he's not though, is he? I mean, he's only just a kid. He's only a few years older than me.

SARAH Of course he's not a real soldier, Dumbo. He just fancies himself. That's why he wears that jacket and the silly hat. I mean, a soldier wouldn't wear a bush hat, would he? Not in winter. Daft.

THOMAS Yeah. That knife he's always messing with an'all. Stupid. And the radio. Anyone'd think there was really someone there, talking back at him.

SARAH My Mum says he's like a savage. All this talk of Gurkhas and stuff. He wants to cut some throats like on the films. She says he needs taking in hand. She says the war'll be the ruination of him, give him daft ideas. She says it's turned him into a bloodthirsty little devil.

THOMAS He frightens me sometimes, Sarah. *Pause* He reminds me of my Dad.

Sarah *stands up and starts kicking at a rock.*

SARAH At least he tells you things though, your Dad. Every time I ask about the war, mine clam up. They treat me like a child. Thomas? *She goes to him and grabs his shoulder* Thomas, look at me. It wasn't really true, was it? What you said about those conscripts? Killing them?

Thomas *won't look at her. She tries to make him.*

SARAH Thomas. Was it really, really true?

THOMAS *looking at his feet, shaking off her hand* I'm fed up with this war. It's spoiled everything. Nothing's any fun no more. It's ruinated.

SARAH Thomas! Answer me!

There is a silence. Broken by a shout. **Michael** *is standing on a ridge.*

MICHAEL   Hey! You two. I've got this great idea. I've been talking to HQ on the radio. We're going to find ourselves a soldier. An enemy. We'll search the area, all right? It's better than finding souvenirs.

Sarah *and* **Thomas** *look at each other, reluctantly.* **Michael** *is insistent.*

MICHAEL   Come **on**. What **else** is there to do? We're going to find ourselves a prisoner of war.

They follow him out.

SCENE THREE

Another part of the moor. **Michael** *has been 'training his troops' by giving them stalking exercises. They have come across the bloody remains of a sheep.*

   Thomas *bursts in first, closely followed by* **Michael**, *who grabs him and stops him from running away.* **Sarah** *follows on, looking disgusted.*

MICHAEL   *fighting the struggling* **Thomas**   You ought to look at it, you know. It'll harden you up for battle. That's important, that.

SARAH   Oh shut up, Michael. You're sick. Let him go. Leave the kid alone.

MICHAEL   *sends* **Thomas** *sprawling*   Dah!

THOMAS   *on his knees, snivelling*   I almost fell in that sheep's guts, I did. It's disgusting. You had me creeping up on it until I almost put my face right in the blood. I'm going to tell my Mum of you.

MICHAEL   Oh dry up, Thomas. You are a little weed. It's necessary training, this. We've got a job to do. We've got to play our part.

SARAH   Did you know it was there? When you made us creep up on it? You really are a little savage, Michael.

MICHAEL   No, I didn't. And I'm **not** a savage, I'm a patriot. We've got to do our bit. It's our duty to be ready. Don't you understand it **yet**, Sarah? There's a war on. We've got to be ready. Vigilant.

6

SARAH You're cracked. It's just a dead old sheep.

MICHAEL Not old, it's new, that's the point. It's not rotten. It's just been hit. It's almost warm.

SARAH Hit by what?

MICHAEL Well a shell I s'pose. It must've been. It shows how close the battle was. Unless . . . unless it trod on a mine.

SARAH *gives a little scream* Michael!

Thomas *starts to run.* **Michael** *grabs him.*

MICHAEL Stand still! Stand still!

They all stand still, exchanging looks. **Thomas** *is whimpering.*

SARAH It couldn't be a mine, could it? Honestly?

MICHAEL *uncertainly* No of course it. . . . No, I don't think. . . . Well.

THOMAS I want to go home. I want my Mummy.

SARAH Ssh. Shush up, Thomas love. Look, we're going soon. We'll get away from here. Just don't move for the moment, all right?

They stand there, thinking.

MICHAEL We can't be in a minefield, I'm sure of it. It's ridiculous. There's nothing here to mine. It's just a stray shell, it must have been. It must have landed in the night and this poor old woolly bought it, that's all. It can't be a minefield.

THOMAS I want my Mum.

MICHAEL We've crawled all over. We've wandered up and down for ages. If it was a minefield we'd be dead by now. As dead as . . . mutton!

Short, uncertain, laugh.

SARAH *faintly* You're sick.

Pause.

THOMAS I want to go. I want to go home.

Pause.

MICHAEL *decision made* Right. That's it. I've had enough of this. I vote we go to the hut. The one with walls. I'm cold. I'm getting out of this wind.

SARAH But the mines. . . .

MICHAEL Oh **knickers!**

He does a sudden wild, stamping war dance all around, shrieking. **Sarah** *and* **Thomas** *clutch each other.* **Michael** *stops, grinning and panting.*

MICHAEL There you are, Weedikins! No mines. Come on, troops. Let's get some shelter, eh?

He stomps off with exaggerated steps. The others follow, with **Thomas** *looking as though he's walking on eggshells.*

SCENE FOUR

The children are outside their second den, a ruined sheep hut. **Michael** *is still insisting they play soldiers, although the others are getting increasingly fed up with him.* **Sarah** *jerks her arm away from him, angrily.*

SARAH Oh leave off, Michael! I'm freezing!

MICHAEL I **still** say we ought to stalk up to it. Just in case.

THOMAS I'm too cold to stalk. Let's just get inside.

SARAH In case of what, anyway? You've got stalking on the brain.

MICHAEL In case we find one. In case there's a soldier hiding in there.

SARAH You're bonkers you are, Michael. What would a soldier be doing here. Think, man.

MICHAEL Well they did say some had got separated off, didn't they? Thomas's Dad said. Over at Foster's Landing. They could be anywhere by now. It's not that far away.

SARAH Oh yes, you've changed your tune. Thomas was a little liar then, wasn't he? It was just a stupid rumour. Thomas was a lying little weed, wasn't he?

THOMAS *to himself* I'm going to tell my Mum of him, anyway.

8

MICHAEL *breaks away and walks, they stay* Ach, I'm fed up of the pair of you.

SARAH And I suppose you'll do like Mr Gregory's meant to have, will you, you divot? I suppose you'll out with your soppy knife and slit his throat. Nutcase.

MICHAEL *turns, whipping out the knife, opening blade, and making a pass with it* If I found one I would. Course I would. They're the enemy. The invaders *Sarcastic* That word Thomas said.

THOMAS Cons . . . cons . . .

MICHAEL No, you fool. *Mickey take* **Rapists!**

THOMAS Oh. Yeah. And. . . .

SARAH *irritable* Oh dry up, Tommy.

She walks up to **Michael**. **Thomas** *follows on. The three of them stop, very close to the shelter now.*

MICHAEL Ssh, anyway. Just shut your mouths, in case. I'll count to three, and then we'll rush it, right? We'll burst in like a hurricane. Ready?

They nod, half playing half tense.

MICHAEL *knife at the ready* One. Two. **Three.**

They rush into the sheep hut, and stop. **Michael** *has his knife at the ready, and* **Thomas** *is pointing a pretend sub-machinegun. Even* **Sarah** *is half joining in the fun. Behind them — unnoticed — is the wounded soldier. He is seated by the doorway, with his back to the wall, and although clearly in agony he is covering them with his swaying rifle. Around his neck are the earphones of a cheap Walkman; the set is on his lap or in his pocket. There is a brief pause. Then* **Thomas** *gets fed up with the game. He turns to look at* **Michael's** *face*

THOMAS *disgustedly, and with daring* See? Bighead! You've got soldiers on the brain. You. . . .

He sees the **Soldier**.

THOMAS *screams* Sarah!

The others turn. They are appalled.

THOMAS Sarah! Mum! Mum! Mum!

He makes a dive towards the door — and towards the **Soldier**
who responds by jerking the rifle onto aim. **Michael** *grabs*
Thomas *savagely round the neck with his left arm. His right*
hand holds the penknife, unconsciously threatening the
Soldier.

MICHAEL   Shut it, Thomas! For God's **sake!** Shut it!

With a shout, **Thomas** *breaks away and hides his face in*
Sarah's *anorak.*

THOMAS   Sarah!

The **Soldier** *has them fully covered.*

End of the first television episode

SCENE FIVE

The **Soldier**, *although extremely weak, manages to keep his*
rifle pointing at the children. **Michael**, *without realising, is*
holding his open knife as if threatening the wounded youth.
After a few moments **Thomas**, *his face still buried in* **Sarah's**
anorak, begins to make a sort of whining noise   Sarah, Sarah,
Sarah, Sarah.

SARAH   There there, Tommy, there there.   *To* **Soldier**
Don't shoot, please. Please don't shoot.

THOMAS   He's going to kill us. He's going to shoot us. He's
going to kill us.

MICHAEL   *faintly*   Shut it, Thomas. Shut it.

Rifle wavers.

SARAH   Please don't shoot us, Mister. We're only harmless
children. Please.

Soldier's *eyes settle on* **Michael's** *knife.* **Sarah** *suddenly*
makes the connection.

SARAH   God you fool! Michael!

She reaches out a hand too quickly and gets a corresponding
gesture from the rifle. She draws back her hand.

SARAH   It's all right, sir. It's all right, honestly.

Very carefully, she moves her hand to the knife. **Michael** *jumps when she touches it, then lets her take it.* **Sarah** *closes it with a click. She drops it.*

SARAH   It's a toy. Do you understand?

THOMAS   *low and whiny*   I want my Mum. Sarah, make him let us go. **Make** him.

MICHAEL   *whispers*   I'm going to make a dash. I'm. . . .

SARAH   No!

Rifle twitches. **Michael** *gulps.*

SARAH   Stand still, Michael. Just stand still.   *Smiles at* **Soldier**   We don't want to hurt you, sir. We're just kids playing.

The **Soldier** *tries to smile back. It turns into a grimace. He lets out a groan. The rifle barrel is almost pointing to the ground.*

SOLDIER   *almost inaudible*   Not hurt. Am cold. Am food. Yo no les lestimaré.

He closes his eyes. The children stare.

MICHAEL   *whispers*   He's useless! We could rush him! We could get that gun and kill him!

SARAH   *anguished whisper*   Shut up! You'll get **us** killed. Shut up!

THOMAS   I want my Mummy. Make him let us go. Sarah!

Soldier *opens his eyes. The gun barrel rises once more.*

SOLDIER   Yo no les lastimaré, ninos. Yo estoy. Am hungry.

Pause.

SARAH   Can we go, sir? Please. We'd better go now, honestly. Will you let us go?

Pause. The **Soldier** *shrugs, then grimaces. The rifle barrel twitches. His eyes close, then open.*

SOLDIER   No tell soldier. Please. Am hurt. No tell soldier.

THOMAS   *hysterically*   My Dad'll do you in, mate! You dirty rapist! My Dad'll bring his. . . .

Michael *hastily stifles* **Thomas's** *shouting.*

MICHAEL   Shut **up.**

The **Soldier,** *startled by* **Thomas,** *jumps. The rifle waves wildly. Then he lowers the barrel to the ground.*

SOLDIER   *very weak*   Friend. Amigo. Por favor — no digan nada a los soldados.

His eyes close. After a few seconds **Sarah** *nudges* **Michael,** *takes* **Thomas** *by the arm.*

SARAH   *whispers*   Out. Go on Tom, get out. Slowly, slowly. Out.

They sidle, silently and fearfully, towards freedom. When they are almost clear, the **Soldier** *opens his eyes. They freeze. He tries to smile.*

SOLDIER   Amigo. Friend. No tell the soldier.

They watch him intently. He makes no move with the rifle. They begin to sidle once more. Suddenly **Thomas** *breaks for freedom, screaming loudly. Then they are all on the move in a scrabbling panic to escape.*

The **Soldier** *tries to move, pauses in agony, tries again. He becomes unconscious.*

SCENE SIX

The sea den with the old radio telephone set. The children are having a serious discussion.

THOMAS   But **why** aren't we going to tell anyone? We've got to. When my Dad finds out he'll **murder** me.

SARAH   He won't find out, though, will he? Unless you tell him, Big Mouth. And even you wouldn't be that stupid, would you?

MICHAEL   I wouldn't be so sure of that. But I tell you this, Thomas. If your Dad does find out, we'll know who told him. And then **we'll** murder you!

THOMAS   But why can't we tell the grown-ups? What are **we** going to do with him in any case?

SARAH Because he said so, didn't he? You heard him, didn't you? He said we weren't to tell the soldiers. You heard him.

MICHAEL He was too busy pooing himself with fright!

SARAH Don't be filthy, Michael. Listen Thomas, it's a **secret**. It's got to be, that's all. If the soldiers found him, I don't know what would happen. Or some of them hotheads, like Mr Gregory, say.

THOMAS They'd put him down like a sick sheep. My Dad said so. The farmers ganged together at Foster's Landing when they found them others. Execution squad. It's dangerous, though. In case they win the war.

MICHAEL Who? The enemy? Don't be ruddy daft, of course they won't! Against the British! You unpatriotic little swine!

SARAH Anyway, whatever **really** happened at Foster's Landing, it's not the point. Whoever found him, it wouldn't turn out good. He might get treated. . . . Well, he said we weren't to tell.

MICHAEL *slyly, after a pause* We didn't say we wouldn't though, did we Sarah? We don't **owe** him anything, do we?

THOMAS Owe him anything! He'd kill us if he got the chance! He's the enemy.

MICHAEL Exactly. We don't owe him a thing. Right, Sarah?

SARAH Well we do owe him something, surely? I mean, he **didn't** shoot us, did he? And he could have done, couldn't he? If he'd wanted to?

THOMAS You're stupid you are, Sarah. Of course he'd kill us. It's his job.

MICHAEL What do you mean, anyway? We owe him 'something'? What could we possibly owe him?

SARAH *confused* Well. You know. I mean, he **is** a human being. We ought at least to get him food and water. I think he's injured. He looked terrible. I think he must have been shot or something. You know.

THOMAS If he was shot, it was our side that did it, wasn't it? If he was shot it was because he was shooting our lot. He's a murderer, stands to reason. He's the enemy.

MICHAEL Exactly. He's the enemy. He's a prisoner of war. Don't you get it yet? Sarah? Don't you get it yet why he's got to be our secret?

SARAH No. I don't know what you're talking about. He's a human being, that's all, and he's injured. We've got to bring him food. What are **you** on about?

Pause.

MICHAEL Look Sarah. Look at it this way. He's the enemy, right? Which **means** if you think about it, he's out to kill the lot of us in the end. He's here to ruinate, destroy.

THOMAS He's a rapist and despoiler.

MICHAEL Shut up Thomas, yeah. He's a ruinator, fair enough. Look Sarah, we didn't ask them in, they just arrived and mucked the whole place up. They've smashed the radios, and the phones, and they've killed sheep and messed up lots of houses. They've put down mines an'all. On the fields. And on the beaches. They've wrecked the place.

THOMAS My Dad says it's wrecked for good. Even when the Brits have seen them off. Even when the Gurkhas have slit their throats and chucked them in the sea. It'll be years before it's safe again. The mines are everywhere. They've ruinated everything. It'll be years.

MICHAEL He's right see, Sarah? There's no denying it. Your little 'human being' up there in the hut — he's just a bloody murderer. It serves him right if he's been hit. It serves him right to suffer. He's a prisoner of war. Ours. **Our** prisoner of war. D'you see it now?

SARAH So what are you suggesting, Michael? What d'you say we should do? Have you got a plan?

Quite a pause.

MICHAEL We've got to kill him, Sarah. We've got to do our bit. We've got to show the grown-ups that we care. It's got to be a proper execution.

Sarah *stands up. Her mouth drops open.*

THOMAS Hey! Hey Michael, that's a good idea. Then my Dad can't tell me off, can he? Hey, that's a good idea.

14

SARAH *quietly* You're joking, aren't you Michael? You're trying to pull my leg.

MICHAEL *staring at her face* No Sarah. I'm serious. Look, either way he dies. If we leave him, he dies of cold and starves. If we tell on him, he dies, the hotheads get him — Tom's Dad and Mr Gregory. My way, we do our bit. We do our bit towards the war, we help. It's our duty, Sarah. It's our duty to the war.

Sarah *moves to leave.*

SARAH Sometimes I wonder about you, Michael. You're insane.

MICHAEL He's going to die anyway, Sarah. You know he is. And if you don't agree it's our duty, you're not a patriot. **Sarah** *leaves* You're a traitor!

THOMAS Sarah! Come back!

MICHAEL Leave her be, Tom, leave her be. She'll do it in the end. Just let her stew a bit.

Thomas, *torn, moves slowly away.*

THOMAS I'm going after her. I won't be long.

MICHAEL *as* **Thomas** *leaves* She'll do it in the end. Just let her stew.

He moves to radio telephone and winds the handle.

MICHAEL Patrol to base. Patrol to base. I read you loud and clear. Destroy the enemy. Destroy. I read you loud and clear. Roger and out.

SCENE SEVEN

Another part of the moor. The children have been arguing. **Sarah**, *very cool, is sitting.* **Michael**, *frustrated, has clearly been haranguing her.*

SARAH *quietly* You can stand there ranting until you're blue in the face, Michael. But it won't make any difference. Unless you agree, I'm not swearing. And that's flat.

15

MICHAEL   But it's stupid, that's all. If we're going to kill him, why bother? Food and blankets and a fire! It's ridiculous.

SARAH   And so are you, Michael. Apart from anything else it might even make it easier, mightn't it? Apart from anything else it might make him easier to approach. He **has** got a rifle, you know.

THOMAS   Yeah. She might have a point Michael. He might think we want to be his friends.

MICHAEL   Oh shut up, you little weed. You just keep out of this.

SARAH   *to Thomas, sarcastically*   You can tell he sees it's sense, Tommy. He's shouting at you!

Michael *makes a threatening gesture at her and she gives him a look: Oh grow up.*

MICHAEL   Anyway, how do I know you'll keep your promise? If you go back to your house for blankets and stuff, how do I know you won't tell?

SARAH   Because I'll have **sworn**, you ratbag! God you're brainless, you are.

THOMAS   I won't tell neither, Michael. I can get the matches easy. I've got them hidden in my drawer. My Dad'd kill me if he knew.

MICHAEL   I don't blame him, you're so thick. It's a wonder you haven't burnt the house down ages ago.

SARAH   Just a little fire, warm him up. A blanket for his legs, maybe a cup of tea and a sandwich.

MICHAEL   And then we kill him?

Sarah *looks shifty.*

MICHAEL   *insistent*   And then we kill him? Right? You'll swear?

SARAH   *brazen*   Yeah. If it comes to . . . .

MICHAEL   That's it, see! You're trying to slide out!

SARAH   *shouts*   I am not. I'll swear. And if it comes to it. All right.

MICHAEL   It will, Sarah, it bloody will. And you'll have **sworn**. Got it? You'll have bloody **sworn.**

16

Sarah *looks up at him with contempt on her face.*

SARAH Yes, Michael. I understand. I'll have sworn. Now dry up about it, eh?

THOMAS *to himself, preoccupied. He's a little worried* She'll never catch me if I'm quiet. They're in the second drawer. She'll never catch me.

Michael *is gazing at* **Sarah**, *who is still sitting, picking at a thread. He is forced to make his decision.*

MICHAEL Right. We swear. Come on. Everyone make a ring. Come **on**, Sarah.

Sarah *stands, and they form a star, with one hand touching in the centre. They walk one circuit in one direction, then reverse, change hands, and walk one circuit in the other direction. Then they hold hands, facing each other in a ring.*

CHANT One, two, three — SWEAR.

MICHAEL My name is Michael. I swear.

Abruptly they do the star ritual once more, then form the ring.

CHANT One, two, three — SWEAR.

THOMAS My name is Thomas. I swear.

Repeat star and ring.

CHANT One, two, three — SWEAR.

SARAH My name is Sarah. I swear.

She immediately breaks the circle and starts to walk off.

MICHAEL *following* Sarah! Where are you going?

SARAH Where do you think, stupid? To be sick? I'm going to make some sandwiches.

She has gone. **Michael**, *almost off, shouts after her.*

MICHAEL Well don't forget, Sarah. You can't go back on a swear. And that's flat.

He leaves, followed by **Thomas.**

SCENE EIGHT

The sea den. **Michael** *and* **Thomas** *enter, talking.*

MICHAEL *as they come in* It's great this, isn't it? It's not a game any more. It's real. Absolutely ace.

THOMAS Do you think she'll do it, though? Do you think she'll go through with it?

MICHAEL She promised, didn't she? She swore like the rest of us? Death to the enemy! Fantastic.

THOMAS She only swore when you gave in, though. It seems daft to me, to get him food and drink and blankets. Then to kill him. It's potty.

MICHAEL Female logic, Thomas. There's no rhyme or reason to it. But never mind, it does no harm to humour them. That's what my father always says.

THOMAS I could see her point in a way. I mean, him with the gun and that. And us with nothing. It might lull him into a . . . you know. . . . Mightn't it?

MICHAEL A sense of false security. Yeah, I s'pose it might. He might even go off to kip if he's got some food in him, and a nice warm blanket on. That'd make life easier. For us.

THOMAS *rather daring; he's subtly taunting* **Michael**
And she didn't give you a lot of choice, in the end, did she? Take it or leave it, she said, suit yourself. It was. . . .

MICHAEL Don't kid yourself, son. I'd have talked her round. But she had a point, I've said so, haven't I? A sense of false security.

Pause.

THOMAS Michael?

MICHAEL Yeah?

THOMAS How you. . . . How we. . . . What exactly are we going to do? To . . . you know . . . kill him?

MICHAEL You're not ducking out are you, Thomas? You're not trying to go back on a swear? Cause if you are. . . .

THOMAS No, no course I'm not. It's just I. . . . Well, I mean, what exactly are we going to do? How do you kill a man?

MICHAEL Well, there's lots of ways, aren't there? I mean, it would be easier if he didn't have a gun, we're going to have to be dead careful. Maybe we can let you sneak up on him and snatch the thing away.

THOMAS *horrified* What! Me! Sneak up on him!

MICHAEL *laughs* I'm pulling your leg, you twit. I wouldn't trust you to take a dummy off a baby. Relax.

THOMAS Crickey, Michael. Don't say stuff like that! But what if he sees us coming, though? What if he shoots us?

MICHAEL He won't. That's why I agreed to let Nelly Knickerleg get the food and stuff. I might get my Mum's sleeping pills or something. Put some in his coffee to make sure. Or even some rat poison from the barn. That'd be another way.

THOMAS But what if they caught you at it?

MICHAEL They might. That's the problem. But I don't think it's necessary, at all. I think we can do it easier, much easier. *He takes out his pen-knife and fingers it* I tell you what though. I don't half wish this was a real commando knife. That would be the easiest.

THOMAS *pause, horrified* Could you knife him, honestly? Groo, I'd throw up. I'd puke.

MICHAEL I'd stick it in his neck and pull. It'd be sharp as sharp. I'd slice it through his jugular and watch the blood squirt. I could do it.

THOMAS Hell, Michael. That's horrible.

MICHAEL *laughs* It isn't a real knife though, is it? No, it'll be a battering job, I reckon. We'll have to batter him.

THOMAS How do you reckon to do it? What will you use, a hammer or something? Will you nick one off your Dad?

MICHAEL 'We', Thomas, not me. No, we won't use a hammer I don't think. Remember where he is. All we've got to do is give him food and keep him occupied. He's in the corner, right? His back's against the wall. While he's noshing, we climb up the outside, or I do, say. Then you or Sarah hands me up a rock. A big one. As big as you can lift. And there you are. We drop it on his bonce. Crunch. A deado. A corpse. Simple. What d'you think?

THOMAS *hardly audible* It sounds all right. We'd better stand well clear though. There could be lots of blood *Pause* It'd be easier, in a way, to let the grown-ups do it, wouldn't it?

MICHAEL Chicken.

THOMAS No I'm not. No. But it'll be hell's messy, Michael. We'd better stand well clear.

MICHAEL *smiles nastily* You'd better run along now, then, and get the matches, like Aunty Sarah said. And make sure you **do**, and some paper if you can, to start the fire. That's all we're asking, Thomas. Just matches and paper, to get a fire going. To lull the enemy. He's going to be comfortable when he dies, this one. **Dead** comfortable.

THOMAS Yeah. All right then, Michael. I'm off. I've got them in my Lego drawer. My Mum doesn't know. I won't be long.

MICHAEL You'd better not be. And remember — you were sworn to secrecy as well. Not a word to anyone. Got it?

THOMAS Yeah, of course I have. Not a word. What are . . . what are you going to do? While we're gone?

MICHAEL I'll go and stand guard. Just in case. Just in case the enemy's getting frisky. In case he tries to escape. Go on. Off you go. And keep your mouth shut.

Thomas *goes. After a pause,* **Michael** *goes also.*

SCENE NINE

Inside the sheep hut, the **Soldier** *is trying to move, presumably to get away. He can barely crawl, and he has to use his rifle as a prop, or crutch. Painstakingly, he manages to reach the doorway, but he is weakening fast. Before he is completely through, he collapses. His rifle falls away from him. The* **Soldier** *tries to raise his head, tries to retrieve the rifle. Then he passes out.*

After a pause, **Michael** *approaches. When he sees the* **Soldier**, *he freezes. Then, very slowly, he moves near. At last, half terrified, he picks up the rifle. He cocks it, and at a range of only a few feet, points it at the* **Soldier's** *head.*

MICHAEL *whispers* I'll kill you, you bastard. You're the enemy.

End of the second television episode

SCENE TEN

Michael holds his aim on the unconscious Soldier for a long time, willing himself to pull the trigger, his body completely tense. He takes the first trigger pressure, then sticks. At last, the Soldier's eyes open. He moves his head. The two of them stare at each other, silent, fascinated. Neither can speak.

Then, very slowly, Michael removes the rifle from his shoulder. He holds it in one hand. He is furious with himself, and confused, and ashamed. The Soldier smiles, painfully.

SOLDIER Por que no me matastes? Muchacho? Why did you not?

Michael kneels and puts the rifle down, almost slamming it to the ground despite the danger of it going off. He walks away from the Soldier. He is almost shouting, to the sky.

MICHAEL It's not **fair**. It's not **fair**! We swore an oath! Together! I **can't** on my own, it's not fair on the others!

He turns to face the Soldier, feeling he has to justify himself, although he does not know for what. He shouts at him.

MICHAEL You wouldn't understand, you Argie pig, you wouldn't understand. It's honour. **We're** not savages. We swore an oath **together**. You wouldn't understand.

They are ten feet or more apart. The Soldier's head is drooping.

SOLDIER Help me. Please. I am very cold. Help me.

Very slowly, Michael begins to walk back to him.

SCENE ELEVEN

Sarah *and* **Thomas** *are walking across the moor.* **Sarah** *is carrying a blanket and a packet of sandwiches;* **Thomas** *a camping kettle with a screw spout, and a milk jug.*

THOMAS *fretfully* Slow down, Sarah, I'm spilling it. Slow down.

SARAH You're useless, Thomas, we can't slow down. There isn't time, we're late already.

THOMAS Fat lot of good it'll be if there's no milk when we get there. Fat lot of good tea is with no milk.

SARAH *stops, because he has. Bitterly* Fat lot of good tea is without a fire, Dumbo. We might as well give up before we start. No matches. One piddling little thing we tell you to get and you don't. A little thing like matches. **And** you said you had some. It was your suggestion.

THOMAS Well, she must have taken them. My Mum. She must have found them. I had them hidden in a drawer.

SARAH Yah, you're full of excuses you are, Thomas Wyatt. You're nothing but excuses. You're useless.

THOMAS What's the hurry, anyway? Stop a minute, Sarah. I need a rest. What's the rush?

SARAH We haven't got much time, that's what. My Mum said. There'll be soldiers everywhere before much longer. That raid last night, the battle. The enemy did lots and lots of damage, they shot down planes and things. There'll be soldiers wandering about, looking for stragglers and that. *She moves back to* **Thomas**, *and pushes him ahead of her. He goes reluctantly* There'll be farmers looking for them, too. Like Mr Gregory's lot. It's only because I said we'd been all round and not seen anyone, that Mum let me out again. I told her that we had a den set up and we needed sandwiches and stuff. But she took some talking to, I can tell you. She was dead against it. And then you hold us up, and you haven't even got the matches. I don't know!

THOMAS *walking ahead now* Well what does it matter, anyway? Why the heck should we care if he's cold or not, or has a cup of tea? We're only going to kill him. Get it over with, I say.

22

SARAH Don't be so bloody daft, kid. Just lift your feet.

Thomas *stops so suddenly that* **Sarah** *walks into him. The jug upends.*

SARAH **Now** what are you doing! You've spilt the lot you silly little sod!

THOMAS What d'you mean 'don't be so bloody daft'? Are you saying we're **not** going to kill him now? Of course we've got to kill him. It's all arranged.

SARAH *she takes the milk jug and looks into it. She makes a noise of disgust* Shchch! Oh God, Thomas. Look, how do you think we're going to do it, then? Poison him? Set fire to the hut? He's got a gun, you fool. He's got a ruddy **rifle**. He's a grown-up **man**.

THOMAS But we'll lull him into a sense of false se . . . thingity. We'll give him tea and blankets. We'll make him go to sleep. And then . . . and then . . . we'll drop a rock on him. We'll smash his head in. Michael said so. He's got it all worked out. . . .

Sarah *hoicks the blanket firmly onto her shoulders, and hands the jug back to* **Thomas.**

SARAH Come on, you'd better not leave it, empty or not. We've got to run.

THOMAS But we've **got** to kill him. We swore an oath. We'll make him warm and comfortable and then we'll smash his head in. Michael said so.

SARAH *starting to walk* You're disgusting you are. That would be cold blood. Murder in cold blood. I sometimes wonder if you're thick or not. Michael's a little monster.

THOMAS *not moving* But **he's** a murderer. He's killed British soldiers in cold blood. It's **him** who's a monster, not us. We've got to kill him. We swore an oath.

SARAH *angrily* Listen, Thomas, pull yourself together and lift your feet up, kid. Michael is a nutcase. It's all a silly game. No one's killing anyone, got it? Nobody. We've got to save this soldier, nothing else. He's cold and hungry and wounded. We've got to save his life. Now **move**.

THOMAS *still immobile* **Save** him? But we can't. We can't. Sarah. We can't save his life. . . .

Sarah realises that there is something going on. She moves back to **Thomas** *and confronts him over the folded blanket. He will not look at her.*

SARAH Thomas Wyatt, just what are you going on about? **Why** can't we save him? **Why?**

THOMAS *tearful* I ran away from the house. My Mum thinks I'm in my room. She caught me messing with the matches, she found me. She told me I wasn't to leave my room 'til my Dad arrived. But I ran away because we were going to kill the soldier. A patriotic duty. And if we don't — they'll kill me. My Mum and Dad. They'll **kill** me. I ran **away**.

SARAH *suspicious and aghast* You didn't tell her? Thomas? You didn't tell her?

THOMAS *looking at the ground* Of course I didn't tell her. Of course I didn't!

SARAH Thomas!

THOMAS No! I didn't, I didn't!

Sarah suddenly drops her bundle and darts foward. She grabs his arm. **Thomas** *cowers, trying to cover his face. She bunches a fist under his nose.*

SARAH You told her, didn't you? You told her! If you don't tell me, Thomas, I'll pummel you. You **told** her, didn't you?

She lets go of his arm, pushing him away. She watches him. **Thomas** *mumbles at the ground.*

THOMAS She didn't believe me, Sarah. I swear it. I said it was a game.

SARAH You told her there was a soldier, injured on the moors.

THOMAS I said it was pretend. I swear it, Sarah, I swear. She didn't believe me.

SARAH You gutless little pig, Thomas. You gutless little swine.

She picks up all her gear, decisively. She starts to walk.

THOMAS But I'm **here.** How can I be gutless? I ran away from my **Mum**.

24

Thomas, *frantically, starts to follow.*

SARAH   And where's your Dad? Oh God! Oh never mind.
Oh glory hallelujah.

She is almost off.

THOMAS   I only did it cause we're going to kill him.
Honestly.

They exit.

SCENE TWELVE

The sheep hut. **Michael** *is crouched beside the* **Soldier,** *who is
sitting with his back to the wall.* **Michael** *has the cassette
headphones on, listening hard. The* **Soldier** *is watching him
almost anxiously.* **Michael** *wants to please, wants to show
friendship, but is puzzled. He takes off the headphones and
smiles helplessly.*

SOLDIER   Madre. . . . Is . . . mother. . . . She says . . . when
come home. . . .

Michael *solemnly hands back the headset. He jumps when he
hears the others.*

SARAH   *outside the shelter*   Michael? Quick. We've got
some food.   *They come in*   You've got a fire going!

MICHAEL   *shamefaced*   Yeah. He had some matches in a
tin.

SARAH   *briskly*   Good. Quick, get this round his legs.

MICHAEL   It's a message from his mum . . . she wants him
to come home. Look Sarah . . . we can't . . . I mean. I tried to
shoo . . . I got the rifle but. . . .

SARAH   *half laughs*   You daft devil, of course you couldn't.
Look, shift! I've got some sandwiches and a kettle full of
water. No milk though. Thomas spilled it all.

MICHAEL   You're not furious? The oath and that? I
thought. . . .

SARAH   Oh do stop wittering. Just get that blanket down.
We understand completely.   *Sarcastic*   **Don't** we,
Thomas?

25

Thomas *flounces into a corner.* **Sarah** *undoes the sandwiches.*
Michael *lays the blanket over the* **Soldier's** *legs*

MICHAEL   What's up with **him?**

SARAH   *putting kettle on fire*   That's the bad news. He's
told, that's what. He's told his rotten mother. I nearly killed
him.

MICHAEL   He's **told!** What does that . . . ? I mean. . . . Oh
glory, Sarah! What are we going to do?

SARAH   *giving sandwiches to* **Soldier**   Here, Mister. Eat
some food. It's corned beef. You'll like that, won't you?

Soldier *tries to smile. He raises sandwich slowly to his mouth.*
He looks sick.

SOLDIER   Thank you. Good children. Your friend . . . good
boy.

He bites slowly, carefully. But **Sarah** *has turned back to*
Michael.

SARAH   He says his mother doesn't believe him but it's not
the point. He says he ran away, she sent him to his room.
But they'll be looking soon, they're bound to be.   *Nodding*
at the **Soldier**   We've got to save him, Michael.

MICHAEL   Who'll be looking? Mr Wyatt and his friends?
Or the army?

SARAH   The army'd be all right. They've got rules. They'd
make him into a prisoner. But if Thomas's Dad. . . . If some
of the hotheads. . . . You know. Like at Foster's Landing.

MICHAEL   You don't think they'd actually. . . . You don't
believe they really . . . when they found those others?
Killed. . . ?

SARAH   Ssh! Look, Michael, no. People don't really . . . it's
just a crazy. . . . But they'd . . . they might be angry. Cruel.
He's just a boy on his own. We've got to get him somewhere
safe. We've got to.

SOLDIER   *he has been listening. He has only taken a few*
bites. He is holding his neck   Army? You talk the army?
Not tell soldiers, no? Please. Not tell soldiers.

He is distressed.

26

MICHAEL   All right, Maria. You'll be all right. Don't you worry, eat your sandwiches.

The **Soldier** *does not eat. He stares at them. He swallows painfully.*

SARAH   Maria?

MICHAEL   That's his name. I think.

THOMAS   But that's a girl's name.

MICHAEL   Oh shut up. Look. Come outside. Everybody.

They move away from the **Soldier** *and look down the moor. He is straining to overhear. They do not want to distress him.*

MICHAEL   Thomas, you've got one more chance. Go down to the bottom of the moor to watch. If you see anyone moving, **anyone**, get back here. **Anyone.** **Thomas** *makes as if to move. Michael grabs his arm.*   And Tom. Don't let them see which way you go. Under **any** circumstances. If you let us down once more, you're for it. Understand?

Thomas *looks at his face and flinches. He nods. Michael shoves him and he runs. They watch him go careering down the hill.*
The **Soldier** *has tried to get closer. He is on his knees.* **Sarah** *hurries to him.* **Michael** *remains outside.*

SARAH   *supporting him, trying to get him to move*   Can you move?! Can you move at all? You've **got** to move, you've got to. We've got to hide you from the men.

MICHAEL   *joins her*   We've got to hide him from bloody Thomas. **Move**, Maria, move.

SOLDIER   Soldiers come? Not tell soldiers.

SARAH   Not the soldiers, no. It's farmers. They're angry. They have guns. The soldiers are all right. We've got to hide you from the men.

SOLDIER   *makes a groaning, crying noise. Doubles over even further*   No. Hurting. Ah. Hurting.

He sinks onto his haunches. They support him, distraught.

SARAH   Lie back. Lie back. Oh Michael, he's in agony.

MICHAEL   *gives up*   Yeah. Come on. Come on, Maria. You lie back. You're not going anywhere. Lie back.

As he helps the **Soldier** *lie down once more and covers him,* **Sarah** *goes to the doorway. She stares across the moors.* **Michael** *joins her.*

SARAH   We should call the soldiers in ourselves. Quickly. It's the only hope. They'll give him drugs and stuff. He'll be a prisoner of war. They'll put him on a stretcher in a helicopter. It's the only hope.

MICHAEL   But he's terrified of them. It must be the enemy propaganda. He must believe that the British Army. . . . It's crazy, Sarah. We're scared of the farmers, and he's scared of the soldiers. And we'll **both** be wrong, it's stupid, stupid, stupid. It's only games, like thinking we could . . . you know. It's all crazy.

SARAH   *terrified*   Oh Michael! Michael! There's Thomas coming! The farmers must be. . . . Oh my God, oh no!

Michael *runs away from the doorway, excited. He shouts back to* **Sarah.**

MICHAEL   No! It's the Army! Sarah, I can see soldiers! I can hear a helicopter! It's the Army!

SARAH   *softly*   The Army. Thank God for that. They've got here first.

Soldier *tries to rise and stumble towards* **Sarah.**

SOLDIER   *calls*   Soldiers. Not tell soldiers. They kill. They kill. Por amor de Dios, no digan nada a los soldados.

SARAH   *smiling gladly, turning to him*   No! They'll save you. The British are coming. They'll save you. Good men! Good! They'll save you!

MICHAEL   *almost off*   They're coming up the hill! A whole platoon of them! Paras! I can see Thomas! He's running, too!

SARAH   *suddenly afraid*   We must tell them.   *Calls* Michael! We've got to explain! We must tell them!

Michael *runs off towards the troops, and* **Sarah** *starts to follow him. The* **Soldier** *makes a desperate gesture to her.*

SOLDIER   *anguished*   Por amor de Dios. They kill!

But **Sarah** *has gone. The* **Soldier**, *using his rifle as a crutch, tries almost frantically to stand and move. The British are* *obviously very close and the helicopter is becoming deafening. The* **Soldier** *is on his knees, at the doorway. He is scrabbling with his rifle.*

MICHAEL   *shouting, off*   He's a boy! He's in the hut! He's harmless, he's just a boy!

SARAH   He's badly hurt! He's a prisoner of war! He needs your help!

The Soldier, *in the entrance, cannot get up. He is frantic. The helicopter and the men are almost at the sheep hut.*

SOLDIER   No tell to soldiers. Por amor de Dios, no digan.

There is a sudden, prolonged burst of gunfire. The **Soldier** *slumps over his rifle.*

SOLDIER   *barely audible*   No digan nada . . . a los soldados.

PRELIMINARY DRAMA ACTIVITIES

The situation in the play is simple — three Falkland children find a badly wounded Argentinian conscript hidden in a sheep shelter. Here are some suggestions which you could use to explore the same kind of situation.

i   Work with a friend. One of you, 'A', is someone who is either on the run from the police or is being pursued by a gang of criminals. Decide who you are and why you are in danger. Your partner, 'B', discovers you hiding in a secret place — perhaps a derelict warehouse or an old barn. Can 'B' persuade you to tell your secret? Will 'B' decide to help you, or to call in the authorities? 'B' may need to ask someone else — perhaps a member of the family or a trusted friend — to help you. How much of the truth about the situation should 'A' tell 'B'?

ii   Work in a small group. One or two of the group, 'A' and 'B', are lost and cannot speak English. But they have an important task to complete, a vital meeting to attend, or an urgent message to deliver. 'A' and 'B' should decide between them what this talk, meeting or message might be.
    The rest of the group discover 'A' and 'B'. Decide on an exact location for this meeting — perhaps a busy railway station or a lonely beach where it won't be easy to find help. Do 'A' and 'B' trust the others, and can they communicate what they want and ask for help without using English? If the rest of the group understand them, is there any way they can help?

iii   Work in twos or threes. One of you is alone in your house at night. Someone knocks at the door and when you open it you see a person covered with blood and very distressed. Nearby you can hear police whistles and sirens. What do you do?

If you decide to shelter the person who asks for help, imagine that a short time later there is another knock at the door. Perhaps this is someone from the police making door-to-door enquiries, or a neighbour who has seen something suspicious. How can you deal with them?

Later, on the television news, there is an item which concerns the person you have helped. What does it tell you about them? Do you regret your actions now you have more information? (You can actually present this news item, either by changing roles, or by using a third person in the group as the newsreader.)

Another news item the following day could say what decisions you made and what happened to the person seeking help.

iv   Imagine that you are working for some secret intelligence organisation — perhaps MI5. You have been called to a special emergency meeting. At this meeting you learn that a suspicious person has been found wandering close to a very secret defence establishment or installation. (Perhaps your teacher or a member of the class could take the job of chairing this meeting.) This stranger seems to have suffered a total loss of memory and cannot answer any questions, but they were carrying a powerful camera, a tape recorder and a small radio transceiver.

Your task is to discover who this stranger might be and what they've been doing. What caused them to lose their memory. If they have really lost it can you help them get their memory back and discover what they were doing? How can you find out if they really have lost their memory? Some members of the class might take on the roles of staff at the secret establishment, perhaps scientists, or military personnel. Alternatively some might be local people. Can you question them and discover something more about the stranger, or find out what has been happening at the secret establishment? What clues can you find?

Your teacher might continue to role-play the head of MI5,

and, if necessary, one of the class might take on the role of the stranger with no memory.

Related reading
You may find it interesting to look at other books exploring a similar theme.

The Deserter, by Nigel Grey (Fontana Lions). A young British soldier who has deserted from his unit in Northern Ireland is found hiding by some English children.
Whistle Down the Wind, by Mary Hayley Bell (out of print, but available from libraries). A group of children who live in the country find a man hiding in a farm building. Through a misunderstanding they come to believe he is Jesus Christ.
The Machine Gunners, by Robert Westall (Puffin). A boy takes a machine gun from a wrecked German aeroplane in World War II. Later, he and his gang find and hide a German pilot.

ACTIVITIES ON AND AROUND THE PLAY

When you are reading or acting the play for the first time, you do not have to read it straight through. When you get to the end of each 'episode', stop to consider what you think will, or should, happen next. Discuss what you would do under those circumstances. You could improvise your own ideas before finding out what does happen next in the play.

When you have finished the play, the issues that it raises and the relationships it shows, can be explored more deeply in your own drama work. Here are just a few suggestions for developing the ideas in the play in your own drama.

i   Work in pairs and use what you know of the characters in the play to act out this exercise. One of you, 'A', is either Thomas, Michael or Sarah. The other 'B', is one of their parents. Something is missing from the house — perhaps some money, an ornament or a piece of jewellery. 'B', the parent, asks 'A', the child, if they know anything about this.

ii   Work with a partner again, but this time reverse the roles so that if you were a parent last time you are now a child. The parent is worried about how the child spends his or her free time and the sort of friends the child mixes with. Again, thinking of what you know of the characters in the play, how would each child react?

iii   How did Thomas break the news of the conscript to his mother? Work with a partner and, using the information in the play, take on the roles of Thomas and his mother. Improvise the scene where he is caught with the box of matches.

If you have taken on the role of Thomas, imagine that you

34

have written a note for your mother and left it in your room for her to find. How will you explain your reasons for running away?

What will Thomas's mother do with the information she has been given by Thomas? Will she tell her husband, or a neighbour, or will she inform the authorities? In pairs, or a small group, explore what happens next — who she tells and how she breaks the news.

iv Sarah is collecting the things the Soldier needs — food, milk, a kettle and some blankets, when one of her parents comes in. How will she explain to them what she wants the things for, without giving away the secret?

v Sarah is persuaded to swear to kill the Soldier, though it turns out that she didn't mean to keep her promise. How do you think Michael persuaded her to swear? What part do you imagine Thomas played in the argument? Again, using the information in the play, improvise the scene with the three children.

vi Most children have their own form of swearing ritual from a simple one like 'Cross your heart and hope to die', to a 'Blood Brothers' ceremony where each person makes a small cut on their hand and then mingles their blood with that of their friend as a pledge that they will never betray each other. Do you have such a ritual? Imagine a situation where you might pledge yourself in this way. Perhaps you are a member of a group about to undertake a dangerous task and each member has to swear secrecy, or it could be a pledge to keep secret a nice surprise for another person, or a dare. Perhaps one member of the group, like Sarah, is reluctant and has to be persuaded. How will you do this?

vii What do you think happened between Michael and the Soldier after the others had left and Michael found he could not kill the Soldier. In pairs improvise the scene. How quickly will Michael change his mind and decide to help the Soldier? How will he find the Soldier's firelighting equipment and end by listening to the cassette recorder. As Michael speaks no Spanish and the Soldier no English how will they make each other understand?

viii(a)   Work in a small group. Imagine that one of you is the Argentinian conscript and the others in the group are members of his family or his close friends. The conscript has been given leave so he can visit his family and tell them about his posting to the Malvinas (the Argentinian name for the Falklands). Decide what kind of family he comes from and whether he is from the country or the town. Has he been away from home before? What will he miss most? What are his feelings about the war? For many Argentinians the retaking of the Malvinas was a necessary, almost holy mission. Does this particular conscript feel like this?

Each member of his family and each one of his friends gives him a farewell present. Depending on what role you are playing, decide what *your* present will be. Start your scene with the family and friends waiting to welcome the soldier. Try to explore the different attitudes you may have to war and conscription in your role. Try to find a strong moment with which to end your scene — perhaps a good luck toast, or the giving of the gifts.

(b)   Arrange the group in a series of 'still photographs' which might show glimpses of the young conscript on other family occasions, and which he might carry with him to remind him of home.

(c)   Playing the role of the young Soldier, write a letter home to a member of your family or to a close friend, telling them what life is like in the army. Your letters should be different depending on the person you are writing to. You will have to decide how much of your real feelings you can share. Or, back in the role of the person you chose to be in the previous exercise, write a letter from home to the Soldier which he might carry round with him.

ix   The British patrol who find the Soldier know that there are armed fugitives in the area. Act out the briefing session by their Officer before they set off. What might their orders be about firing on, or taking prisoner, any Argentinian soldiers they find?

x   Show how each child explains what has happened to their parents on the evening after the event. Are their parents relieved/angry/upset/proud?

xi After the war, the children obtain the Soldier's family address in Argentina. Either write a letter from each of them or a joint letter explaining what happened. Which of the Soldier's possessions would the children most like to return to his family with the letter?

xii At the end of the armed conflict, Sarah, Michael and Thomas would have to go back to school. How do you think their school friends would react to them? Would they be excited, interested in the gory details, or not believe them? How do you think each of the three children would react to the questions? Might Michael, for example, go back to being the boastful, war-mongering boy he was at first? Reconstruct what you imagine might happen on the children's first day back at school.

xiii The war is over and the young Soldier's mother has come to the Falklands to see her son's grave. She has asked to meet the children so that she can find out exactly how her son died. Work in a small group and take on the roles of the three children and the conscript's mother. How will the children tell her about her son's death? Will they be quite truthful about their part in what happened?

xiv Decide what is to be written on the Soldier's headstone. Invent a name for him and any factual details which you feel are necessary. Add an appropriate inscription or quotation.

xv Write the notice of the Soldier's death which might appear in his local newspaper in Argentina. How will the facts of his death be presented? Will the news be reported differently if it is published after the war is over?

xvi It has been decided that a monument should be built to commemorate the soldiers who fought in the war. Work in a group of about four or five, and decide whether your monument will commemorate the British soldiers, the Argentinians, or whether it will be a memorial to the soldiers of both sides who died in the fighting. Using the people in your group, create a 'statue' which will be the memorial. You can use all the people in your group, or only as many as you feel are necessary. When your statue is finished, decide on the title or inscription which will be carved on its base.

xvii   The story of *A Game of Soldiers* could have been very
different. The Soldier might have taken the children hostage.
In small groups work out what would have happened in that
case. How would the children get a message to their families
and how would their families and the army react then?

THE TELEVISION
SCRIPT

Naturally enough, things can be achieved using film and
television technology that cannot be done on stage. Here are
two extracts from the original television script which differ
widely from the printed text.

The first is not included in the stage version at all. Why do
you think this is, and do you consider that it *could* be
performed? If so, how? If you have seen the play on televison,
how did it differ on screen from this shooting script?

The second scene is in the printed play, but takes a very
different form to that of the television script. Compare the
two versions, and analyse how and why they differ.

If you have access to video or film equipment you might like
to film these short sections, adapting them yourself to suit the
resources and effects available. You might, for instance,
consider using models and artwork and replica soldiers to
convey the Falklands landscape, the helicopter and so on. You
could also make comparisons between television and staging
techniques.

Even without equipment, you could get a good idea of how a
film or television crew would work by using 'mocked-up' or
improvised cameras and microphones.

Extract One

SCENE ONE
Exterior : Moorland : Night 1

*Across a waste of moorland we see the flashes, and hear the
noise, of a battle. Close to us, at the end of a long wet ditch, is a
hunched shape. It could be a corpse. Over the skyline, someone*

is running, and staggering. It is a young **Soldier**, *pulling a rifle by the barrel, using it as a walking stick. He reaches the head of the ditch as a flash occurs, and falls into it. His face is white and bloody. He is very young. He sprawls full length. A heavy naval gun fires rhythmically in the distance.*

SCENE TWO
Interior : Thomas's Bedroom : Night 1

The rhythm of the naval gun is broken by bursts of lighter firing. **Thomas** *is asleep, his face and the bedroom wall illuminated by pale flickers through the curtains. He is disturbed, and whimpers in his sleep. There is a louder explosion, and* **Thomas** *wakes. He lies there, frightened, listening and watching the flickering.*

THOMAS   *calls, but not loudly*   Mum. Mum. Mum.

A loud detonation.

THOMAS   *still not loudly: he is afraid to wake up his mother and father. It is forbidden to call out in the night*   Mum. *More anguished.* Muuum.

He gets out of bed and goes to the door. He puts his hand on the knob and turns it fearfully.

SCENE THREE
Exterior : Moorland By Dead Sheep : Night 1

The **Soldier** *is slumped in the water at the bottom of the ditch. He begins to crawl along it, dragging his rifle like a dog. He is not far from the corpse/shape. He is obviously in pain, and grunts as he moves.*

SCENE FOUR
Interior : Passageway in Thomas's House : Night 1

Slowly, he approaches his parents' door. There is a light shining underneath it. Thomas stands outside.

THOMAS   *very quietly*   Mum. Dad. Mum.

There is no answer. **Thomas** *sits down very carefully and quietly and leans against the door jamb. He puts his hand in the spill of light, for comfort. He puts his head near the door*

40

and listens. *From inside, adult voices can be heard in conversation. We cannot hear what is being said.*

There is a sudden, very loud explosion. **Thomas** *jumps. He calls involuntarily.*

THOMAS Mum! Mum!

Silence. Then a bed creaks.

DAD *loud* Thomas! Get to bed immediately! Thomas? If you're outside this door!

Thomas *scuttles down the passageway. As he closes his door, his parents' is jerked open.* **Father's** *angry face. The passage is empty.*

SCENE FIVE
Exterior : Moorland By Dead Sheep : Night 1

In the ditch, the **Soldier** *has reached the shape. He puts out a hand, tentatively. He feels. Then pulls it back with a noise of horror. He puts it close to his face and we see that it is covered in blood.*

There are a series of flashes. We see the **Soldier's** *face plainly. And the bloody remains of a sheep, a grinning head and a damaged body. It has apparently been blown up.*

Cut To Black

'A GAME OF SOLDIERS'
by
JAN NEEDLE
Episode One

SCENE SIX
Exterior : Moorland Near Farmhouse : Morning 2

Sarah *in jeans, jersey and anorak, is walking alone across the moor, eating toffee from a paper. She is making for a tumbledown shelter affair. As she approaches, the camera suggests that someone is lying in wait for her. We assume it is the wounded soldier.*

SARAH *as she approaches the shelter* Michael! Michael! Thomas! Tommy?

She stops and looks at her watch. To herself Typical!

41

Sarah, *back to camera, from watcher's p.o.v. combat-jacketed arm foreground.*

SARAH Michael? Are you hiding?

With a horrible roar, **Michael** *jumps on* **Sarah's** *back. He bears her to the ground.* **Sarah** *screams.*

SCENE SEVEN
Exterior : Farmhouse : Morning 2

A long shot of **Thomas's** *house, from a high point.* **Thomas** *is at the back door, with his* **Mother,** *who appears to be lecturing him. We can't hear what is being said. His* **Father** *emerges. He joins in briefly, points across the moor, wags his finger at* **Thomas.**

SCENE EIGHT
Exterior : Moor Near Farmhouse : Morning 2

Camera starts on toffee bag lying discarded. Pan off to find **Sarah** *and* **Michael** *as dialogue starts.*

MICHAEL My God, no wonder he's always late for everything. Earache, earache, earache. Don't they ever let up on him?

SARAH Well he **is** only eight I s'pose. I s'pose they worry about him because of that.

Cut to see that **Sarah** *and* **Michael** *are watching* **Thomas** *and his parents.*

MICHAEL Nuts. His Dad's a pain, that's all. He never lets him alone. He can't even breathe without asking permission these days.

SARAH Here he comes.

Thomas *has left his parents and started running towards the ridge. He is immediately called back.*

MICHAEL I don't think! Look at the old devil now. **Thomas's** *Father is bending over him* It's ridiculous.

SARAH There is a war on. Still, I'm glad my Mum and Dad don't carry on like that. They just told me to be careful, that's all.

Thomas *is away now. He hares up the hill towards them.* **Michael** *and* **Sarah** *stand up.*

THOMAS *waving* Sarah! Michael! Wait for me! Wait for me! **Sarah** *and* **Michael** *start to run* Wait for me!

Extract Two

SCENE TWENTY
Exterior : Shelter : Day 2

Sarah *looking over wall in outer yard.* **Michael** *joins her.*

SARAH We should call the soldiers in ourselves. Quickly. It's the only hope. They'll give him drugs and stuff. He'll be a prisoner of war. They'll put him on a stretcher in a helicopter. It's the only hope.

MICHAEL But he's terrified of them. *Turns and sits* It's crazy, Sarah. We're scared of the farmers, and he's scared of the soldiers. And we'll both be wrong, it's stupid, stupid, stupid. It's only games, like thinking we could . . . you know. It's all crazy.

SARAH Oh Michael, Michael, there's Thomas coming. The farmers must be. . . . Oh my God, oh no.

SCENE TWENTY-ONE
Exterior : Moor By Shelter : Day 2

We see **Thomas**, *running towards shelter from* **Sarah** *and* **Michael's** *p.o.v. The helicopter is heard.*

It appears, then looms, behind **Thomas**, *low, and seems to follow him. He is shouting, screaming, inaudibly as it passes over him.*

SCENE TWENTY-TWO
Exterior : By Shelter : Day 2

MICHAEL *softly* The Army. Thank God for that. They've got here first.

Sarah *and* **Michael** *hold each other, or smile, in great relief.*

SOLDIER *calls from doorway* Soldiers. Not tell soldiers. They kill. They kill. Por amor de Dios, no digan nada a los soldados.

SARAH *smiling gladly, turning to him* No! They'll save

you. The British are coming. They'll save you. Good men!
Good! They'll save you! We'll tell them.

SCENE TWENTY-THREE
Exterior: Moor : Day 2

Low angle. **Thomas** *running. He falls and behind him we see
the soldiers. Helicopter noise in evidence.*

SCENE TWENTY-FOUR
Exterior : Moor by Shelter : Day 2

*Helicopter noise in evidence throughout. Different angle. See
officer lift* **Thomas** *to his feet. They are joined by* **Sarah** *and*
Michael.

Soldiers run on out of shot towards hut.

MICHAEL   *shouting*   He's a boy! He's harmless! He's just a
boy!

SARAH   *shouting*   He's badly hurt! A prisoner! He needs
your help!

SCENE TWENTY-FIVE
Exterior : Shelter : Day 2

Cu shelter doorway. See **Soldier** *raise rifle. He is obviously
panic-stricken. Attempting to take aim.*

SCENE TWENTY-SIX
Exterior : Moorland : Day 2

The **Children**, *backs to camera, are gesturing wildly to the
officer.*

*We hear, suddenly and loudly over the helicopter noise, a short
volley of gunfire.*

Children *turn to camera.*

Freeze.

Cut to black

End Credits

44

STAGING THE PLAY

This version of the play is intended to be extremely flexible and you should feel free to adapt the text in any way you think appropriate. Various parts may be found to be unsatisfactory or unworkable in certain circumstances, and these could be cut or adapted. You may, for example, find screams both difficult to do and likely to provoke unwelcome laughter.

Likewise, should you have difficulty learning the lines, or find that in learning them they become wooden, use your own words and treat the text as a framework. It is not sacred.

The play can be performed with one cast of four or, since most school groups will be larger than this, with three groups of four, taking one 'section' each. You might consider adding scenes, or even bringing on the soldiers at the end.

The age of the children in the play is obviously important, but don't be put off by this. You will all remember what it was like to be eight, and it is a good acting exercise to portray a young child without making others laugh.

Although *A Game of Soldiers* could be staged on the school hall stage, most school stages are not the best or most exciting places to put on a play. Probably, it can be staged most effectively in the 'round', drawing the audience into the action and giving more scope for imaginative use of the acting area (For example see the drawing on p. 46.)

Setting, props and costume, as indicated in the text, are all very simple and should be readily available from your drama wardrobe, or begged, borrowed or stolen from brothers, sisters, parents and the like. The radio telephone can be easily mocked up, or even become an imaginary prop — part of Michael's 'game of soldiers'.

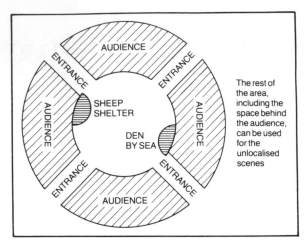

The rest of the area, including the space behind the audience, can be used for the unlocalised scenes

Wherever the piece is played, some staging decisions will have to be made early on. The following suggestions are intended as a guide; there will be other solutions that are just as valid.

Firstly, you will have to decide when and how the Soldier is brought into the acting area and whether he is to be fully, partially, or not visible throughout the play, even when he is not involved in the action. He could even come on before the action starts, but if he is to be there as a presence he must not be there as a distraction. Among other things, therefore, you must make sure he is comfortable!

If the play is in the round, the use of different parts of the area, including that behind the audience, can be exploited to great effect.

If there is no tape or cassette recorder available for the sound effects — helicopter and gunfire — at the end, a certain amount of thought and experiment will be needed. You will certainly be able to make it work, however. The sound of a single shot, for instance, can very easily be achieved physically, even if you cannot borrow the PE teacher's starting pistol.

THE PEOPLE INVOLVED

During and after the Falklands crisis, some of the people who were directly involved in the conflict wrote of their experiences, thoughts, and feelings. Here are extracts from the diaries of an Argentinian sergeant and two Falklands families, and from the letters of Lieutenant David Tinker, RN, who was killed on HMS Glamorgan two days before the Argentinians surrendered. Following the extracts are suggestions for further work.

Extracts from Stuart Wallace's Diaries

A MOVING account of life in the Falklands during the Argentine occupation emerged yesterday from the diary of an islander.

Stuart Wallace was marked out by the junta as a 'subversive'. With his wife Lilian, 27, and their two small children, Fiona, four, and 18-month-old James, he came under the frighteningly close attention of Argentina's political controllers.

Stuart, a 27-year-old worker at Port Stanley's Cable and Wireless Company, was shipped away to a remote settlement with his family, to live out the rest of the occupation in isolation, while their friends and relatives desperately sought information about them.

This is their story from first to last — Stuart's personal diary of the occupation.

APRIL 1: The first I knew was when the governor came on the radio and said that an invasion was imminent.

He asked for all members of the Falkland Island Defence Force, which included me, to report to our drill hall headquarters. The scene there was amazing. People were preparing the magazines for their rifles and asking what was going on.

Later, the Governor came on the radio again and declared a state of emergency. There was a sense of numbness, we just could not believe it.

I went home, and that night sat up late with Lilian listening to the radio. We were just sitting there drinking gallons of tea, with the children asleep in bed. Patrick Watts, who runs Falkland Island Radio, came on to say the invasion force was off Cape Pembroke.

APRIL 2: Early that morning the firing broke out. We could hear them mortaring the Marines at the Moody Brook barracks.

Sinister

The children woke up as the first small arms fire was crackling away in the distance. It was getting closer all the time, and there were people outside in the streets shouting and vehicles racing through town.

I tried to get to the office, but by then the fighting was all around us. Marines were out in the streets and gardens firing at the invaders.

Lilian made us breakfast of tea and toast. Fiona kept asking: 'Daddy, what is the banging?' and James was crying.

From my garden I could see red tracer curving through the air. The Marines were in the back of my garden and one, very coolly suggested I went back in and got down on the floor. We stayed crouching on the kitchen floor and Lilian produced board games for the children to play with.

We heard Argentine armoured personnel carriers rumbling up the street and I thought many people must be dead.

Governor Rex Hunt came on the air and announced we'd surrendered.

The Daily Mail 28 June 1982

47

Extracts from Sergeant Victor Bustamente's Diaries

SHORTLY after 9 p.m. on June 14 — the day Argentina's garrison commander surrendered the Falklands — a British intelligence officer found a well-thumbed notebook in a plastic bag at Port Stanley post office. It contained a remarkable record of the conflict, seen through the eyes of Argentine Sergeant Victor Bustamente.

He reveals his compassion for the enemy. And the pain of being parted from his wife Estela and five-year-old son Lucio. Sergeant Bustamente, 29, thought as he wrote that he might never see them again. But he lived through the fighting and is now back home in Buenos Aires.

Many times since, the sergeant has wondered what became of his 33-page record of war. Told that it had turned up intact he said : "Thank you many hundreds of times."

April 14:

02.25: Landed in the Islands. Hurricane gusts of wind. Between 3 and 4 degrees below zero. 08.00: We go with the major towards the town. Slow journey. Evening camp.

Uncle not yet arrived. As on first trip only half the company moved. We are going to sleep, tranquil and content.

I think a lot of my boy and my wife. I imagine how they must be and am uneasy. My family still does not know I am here. Perhaps tomorrow I'll write and let them know.

April 17:

. . . The great majority think that nothing will happen and soon we'll be going from here. Personally I don't share this idea. Please God I am mistaken.

April 19:

A leaden day. Troops continue arriving and the place is becoming converted into a fortress. Let's hope nothing happens.

April 20:

I believe that the nearness of the pirate fleet (the British Task Force) has begun to worry more than one person . . . I feel a bit afraid about what I think is inevitable — open hostilities.

I pray to God that the matter is solved peaceably because, if not, it is going to be a massacre for both sides.

April 21:

I learned that part of the fleet is nearing the Gorgias (South Georgia). According to the news, negotiations are at zero point.

April 24:

Very preoccupied. Reports of imminent attack against Gorgias. Here most people are quite unworried. I am going to sleep.

British forces retook South Georgia the following day without casualties.

April 29:

I heard Costa Mendez warned on the radio of the imminence of a British attack on the Malvinas (Falklands) . . . We are all convinced we are fighting for a just cause. The morale of the troops is good.

In my opinion they have not adopted the proper measures as regards the Islanders. They go about by themselves and engage in activities highly suspect.

I had a letter from Estela and Lucio's sketches. They made me cry but this gives me greater strength to win and return. For them I'll do it.

April 30:

Wrote again to Estela and Mama. When I can I'm going to visit uncle. The chap's all right, dug in a hole like a mole.

More optimistic today about a negotiated solution.

The start of the British assault on the Falklands was signalled on May 1 by a Vulcan bomber raid on Stanley airfield. Next day a British submarine torpedoed the Argentine cruiser General Belgrano.

May 1:

The thing has begun. Since 4.40 in the morning the radio has been insistently repeating red alert. There were dramatic moments. The anti-aircraft guns almost didn't fire.

The plane dropped a couple of bombs on the airport. Intermittent air and naval bombardment. Long tense, hours.

May 2:

Everybody today is going about with helmets on and rifles shouldered.

We are all waiting. Nobody walks in the streets. Curfew was imposed at 18.00 hours. Ferrari, the fat one, is sleeping.

Daily Mirror 20 July 1982

Extracts from John Smith's Diaries

AS SOON as 43-year-old John Smith knew the Argentines had invaded, he decided to keep a diary. It was the beginning of a 70-day ordeal for Smith, his wife Heen, and their four children — Jeremy, 19, Martyn, 18, Anya, 15, and Tyssen, 10. And that ordeal is chronicled graphically, day-by-day, from the first dark days of the invasion to the joyful moment when British soldiers marched back into Port Stanley. Until last year when he retired, Mr. Smith was a section manager with the Falkland Islands Company.

MAY 19

VERY foggy. Woke very depressed, decided to fight it with good clear up in study, though is it worth it as it may all be blown to bits in a few days time. Decided not to listen to the BBC for today.

Harrier raid at lunchtime.

Bucked up in afternoon to Mass at 3 o'clock, passed many troops preparing to go into the hills, terribly pathetic sight. Tired, cold, hungry with blank confused faces, some must have been in the same clothes for six weeks.

Officers still as well fed and arrogant as ever. Must fight depression in future.

MAY 20

ANOTHER noisy night in bunker, naval bombardment started about 11:30 which now has a horrific effect on me so I slept soundly until 7:30. Early this morning lorry loads of troops suddenly arrived to fill in huge trench-cum-bunker they'd dug opposite the house on the Co-op corner.

They said there had been a fire in there but seems unlikely. Personally I think they may have been filling it with their dead from last night's bombardment. It's odd for them to be filling in holes.

MAY 21

GREAT news. Brits ashore at Port San Carlos. This is what we've all been waiting for.

Great confusion about three this afternoon fighter over harbour very low. Argentine TV crew filming it. Some troops rushing about with weapons, other continued their cigarettes, then anti-aircraft guns opened up and shot it down, which was a bit embarrassing for them, as it turned out to be one of theirs.

About four this afternoon a soldier was posted outside our house done up like an arsenal with pistol, rifle, grenades and smoke canisters.

MAY 22

OUR guard outside again. Soon got him in with food and this time he told the truth, only one small meal per day, he's very hungry, sleeps in a hole on the hill half full of water. His clothing made great wet patches on the carpet.

This charity exercise was worthwhile — it gives us some idea of the state of war from the Argies' side.

Just heard dreadful news that Ardent has gone at PSC. But Brits are well dug in.

Daily Express 29 June 1982

49

Extracts from David Tinker's letters

HMS Glamorgan,
April 2, 1982

To H and E,

Thank you for your long letter. This is just a quick one to say that today we have heard the news that we are off to the Falkland Islands to bash the Argentinians. This is great fun, and very much like Maggie Thatcher to stick up for our few remaining colonies with a show of force! A great fleet is assembling...

Of course, the whole thing may blow over in a week, but the thrill of some real confrontation away from the nuclear bombs of the northern world in a 'colonial war' is quite exciting compared to the usual dull routine of excercises and paperwork...

The Captain is of course delighted: he may be able to finish his career in a blaze of glory... All for now, as this must be posted before the ships separate and we head south for the penguins.

HMS Glamorgan,
April 2, 1982

To Christine,

We are off to the Falkland Islands as you have probably heard on the news to do a bit of Wog-Bashing! There's a terrific force of ships assembling...sixteen British warships steaming south across the Atlantic at a great rate of knots - terrific!

It reminds me that in the Great War...Britain sent absolutely everything down to the Falklands and gave the Germans a real pounding... This really is like the days of 1914 and great fun...

Unless you hear anything on the radio or in the newspapers to say that we are coming back you will have to work on the assumption that I probably won't be back until July.

HMS Glamorgan (No date,
received April 16)

To H and E,

Just a quick note to say that we are all fine and having fun playing our war games. One advantage of the Falklands is that you have to go through the tropics first, so we are all getting a good sun tan...

We are now resplendent in our war-paint...but these days of course it is all space-age stuff and not so much like the films where they took off their white cap-covers on the bridge before a battle and had duffle-coats and cocoa (although both would be very welcome where we are going).

HMS Glamorgan, April 7

To Christine,

If it does come to a war there won't be much of a naval battle.
Our submarines can take out their aircraft carrier and Type 42s (built in
Barrow!) and we can take care of the rest... The main threat is from
air attack...

The most amusing thing is that it will be difficult to find
the Falkland islanders. With only 1,800 of them, there are, I suppose,
15,000 RN personnel, 4,000 army — 4,000 Argentinian army, and say 3,000
Argentinian navy: outnumbering the islanders by about twelve to one!

The good thing about it is that there is stacks of time left
for some sort of compromise. Which I am sure will happen.

HMS Glamorgan, April 10

To Christine,

My guess is that I won't be back for some time - probably
September... It all depends on whether a settlement can be reached, but
even then we may be left to patrol the area...

As we get nearer we have lost the euphoria - accompanied by
depression - and are getting more determined that we must do our job well
to defeat the Argentinians and survive. Reality is dawning rapidly.

At times the situation seems so absolutely silly: here we
are, in 1982, fighting a colonial war on the other side of the world:
28,000 men going to fight over a fairly dreadful piece of land inhabited
by 1,800 people. After it is all over and millions of pounds have been
expended they will be left in peace (having had their homes destroyed by
shelling) and the 28,000 men will then go away again. Moreover, one side
(Britain) has supplied the other with its weapons so that the war can be
started in the first place - and both sides end up impoverished.

The ideal is most praiseworthy: the wishes of a tiny people
being supported by the might of a large industrialised state. Everything
else is quite ludicrous.

HMS Glamorgan, May 25

To Gordon and Marion Hayes,

It is a very odd feeling being at war out here.
We are so used to exercises that it is not particularly different, only
much more tense... We fire our guns and we get attacked and in between
we try to carry on our lives at sea as if nothing had happened...

Of course, what is happening here must feel
familiar to you from the Second World War: the bravery and courage of
our own pilots...and the bravery and tragic waste of life of the Argentinian
pilots, sent against overwhelming anti-aircraft missiles by heartless
superiors. The devotion to duty of our frigates in the Falklands Sound,
who were sitting ducks for the Argentinian aircraft and which were all hit
by bombs. And above all, the tragedy, anguish, and horror of the British
lives that have been lost: which have been spent quite willingly by
Mrs Thatcher and Mr Nott to make up for the political ineptitude and
pig-headedness of the Government. When one considers the total sorrow,
financial loss, loss of ships for Britain (which I doubt will ever be
replaced) and destruction to the Falklands - now dotted with war graves
- all balanced against a 'principle', a flag, and the ousting of two
dozen islanders it does seem to me personally the most pointless of wars
ever fought by Britain.

HMS Glamorgan, June 8

To H and E,

...Lots of love for now; I will write again soon.

David Tinker was killed in action on June 12, 1982, when the Glamorgan was hit by an Exocet missile which had been made in France. His body was committed to the sea the same night, with those of his twelve comrades who also died. He was 25 and left a widow, Christine.

i   Imagine that you are one of the children in the play, or the young Soldier. Write a diary in which you record the various events of the play. If you choose to be the Soldier, your diary may be very brief. Look carefully at the play and work out which incidents would be most important for your character to write about. If you can, show how the events changed that person's attitudes, as David Tinker's attitudes were changed.

   If the young Soldier was not fatally wounded by the Army, but recovered and went home to Argentina, explore what he might say to his family and friends about his experiences. Would he be able to convey his feelings to people who had not shared his experiences?

   Write a short poem from the point of view of the young Soldier, called 'War' or 'The Conscript'.

ii   After an incident like the one in the play, an official enquiry would have to be held. Set up a formal enquiry in your classroom. Choose roles either: as the children, their parents, neighbours, the British officer in charge of the patrol and some of his men, a Falklands farmer, an Argentinian officer who has been taken prisoner. Each person who has anything to report to the enquiry should speak formally and present their statement carefully. Some members of the class and your teacher may choose to become the tribunal who are hearing the enquiry. They will want to ask questions and find out details of what happened. Is everyone who gives evidence to the enquiry telling the whole truth? Will any facts emerge about other incidents on the islands?

   The members of the tribunal may make an official statement to the press and those who have given evidence could be asked to put their evidence in writing. Make sure that what you write is appropriate to the role you have taken on for the enquiry.

THE QUESTION OF SOVEREIGNTY

When you listen to the big wheels talk, they're making war for reasons of piety, in the name of everything that's fine and noble. But when you take another look, you see they're not so dumb; they're making war for profit. If they weren't the small fry like me wouldn't have anything to do with it.

BRECHT. *Mother Courage*

-We shall defend our island, whatever the cost may be, we shall fight on the beaches, we shall fight on the landing grounds, we shall fight in the fields and in the streets, we shall fight in the hills; we shall never surrender.

WINSTON CHURCHILL. *House of Commons, 4 June 1940*

At heart, the Falkland war was a dispute over who should have sovereignty over a group of rather barren and insignificant islands in the South Atlantic. It is a dispute that has rumbled on for many many years and is unlikely to be easily resolved. The following chronology of events will give you some idea of the complexity of the problems involved.

The Falklands Question — A Chronology

1598 A Dutchman — Sebaldus van Weerdt — landed on the Falklands. He was accepted as the discoverer.

1764 The French established Port Louis on East Falkland. The French called the islands Les Isles Malouines, because sailors from St Malo used them frequently as a staging post. Hence the Spanish, Las Islas Malvinas.

1766 January The British established the first West Falkland habitation.

1766 October Spain bought Port Louis from France.

1770 Britain expelled from West Falkland by Spain.

1771 Britain reoccupied West Falkland after Spain withdrew.

1774 Britain withdrew, leaving a plaque stating their claim. Spain returned. Both islands run by Spain until 1808.

1810 The United Provinces of the Rio de la Plata, which included the forerunner of Argentina, were set up. Spanish rule in South America ended.

1811 Spain formally ended any claim on the Falklands.

1820 Buenos Aires — which was to become Argentina — claimed the unoccupied islands for the United Provinces as inheritors of the Spanish dominion.

1824 Louis Vernet granted settlement rights on East Falkland. A 'commandant of the Malvinas' appointed.

1828 Vernet granted sovereignty of East Falkland.

1829 June Buenos Aires claimed sovereignty over both islands.

1829 August Britain claimed sovereignty over both islands.

1832 December to **1833 January** HMS Clio took West Falkland, then East Falkland, expelling representatives of the Buenos Aires government.

1910 A British Foreign Office memorandum suggested that at the time of the Clio action, Argentina possessed a better legal claim to the islands than Britain.

1982 March 19 Argentinian flag raised on South Georgia.

1982 April 2 Argentinians invaded East Falkland.

1982 April 3 United Nations Security Council called on Argentina to withdraw.

1982 April 5   First ships of British Task Force set sail.

1982 April   When the conflict began, a set of public documents relating to sovereignty were removed from the Public Records Office by Foreign Office officials.

1982 June 14   Argentinian troops surrendered.

1983   Lord Avebury, the Liberal peer, suggested that the Government was attempting to suppress the documents because they cast 'serious doubt on Britain's claim to sovereignty'.

Present day   Both British and Argentinian governments continue to insist that sovereignty of the islands is theirs. The House of Commons was told early in 1983 that an official document relating to a British plan in 1940 to reunite the Falklands with Argentina would not be released until at least 1991.

The following letter which appeared in *The Guardian*, gives another interesting perspective on the debate.

Why none of us, not even the Falklanders, has the right to exist on our own terms

Sir,—I am Argentine. I settled here 12 years ago as an architect. My wife is English and we are about to have our first baby. I hope it is evident from these facts that I have as great a personal interest in the improvement of Anglo-Argentine relations as Martin Dodds (Letters, February 1) professes to have. Unfortunately the attitudes behind his letter will contribute very little towards achieving it.

The gist of his letter is that discussions on sovereignty are not possible for three reasons: Argentina's claim to the islands is not as good as that of the islanders themselves; although Mr Alfonsin is a welcome change, the next government (which in his view can only be either Peronist or the army) will renege on any guarantees given by him; and there can be no lasting solution to the problem unless the islanders' right to exist on their terms is recognised.

Over the last decades it has become evident that the islanders will not talk to anyone about transfer of sovereignty: dictators are unpalatable, democrats unreliable and their guarantees not credible. On this line of thought, there must be quite a few Poles still wondering about the credibility or ultimate effectiveness of British and French guarantees.

The only lasting arrangements are those that correspond with the realities of the situation in question, and this has very little to do with the moral qualities or blemishes of the parties concerned. I do not like the Argentine generals any more than Mr Dodds does, but if he wants to live in the South American continent, he has to accept the continent's reality.

The islanders will not accept talks on anything other than the supply of necessities from the Argentine mainland. I appreciate

55

that this might be of great importance to them and useful to Britain if it avoids having to ship the lavatory paper from Portsmouth; the relevance to Argentina, if sovereignty is not mentionable, escapes me.

If the Falklands are to be anything but part of Argentina's sovereign territory, I cannot imagine that the supply of groceries to a market of 1,800 people justifies talks between governments or the forfeiture by Argentina of the right to what it considers its territory. Argentina might be forced to enter into discussions through pressure on issues which have nothing to do with the islands — i.e. the external debt — but if that happens we are into the realm of stick-and-carrot negotiations, not the grand moral principles invoked by Mr Dodds.

He mentions the islanders' right to exist on their own terms. This is a privilege denied to most of us: I doubt if the queen lives life on her own terms, and Indian peasants certainly do not. For most of us, life is coming to terms with the limitations of our reality, and making the most of the opportunities available within them: I fail to see why the Falkland Islanders are a different case from the rest of mankind.

In the short term, the islanders have got the situation exactly as they want it: the Union Jack flies, money is poured in, sovereignty is unmentionable to Mr Kinnock, Mrs Thatcher or anyone else concerned, bar Mr Alfonsin. How long will this last, and what will come next is a different matter.

It would be more useful if Mr Dodds put his mind to thinking about these last points rather than in finding reasons to preserve the present situation.—Yours sincerely.
Guillermo Gil.
1 Lyndhurst Road,
London NW3.

The Guardian February 1984

i In small groups, discuss who you think should have sovereignty over the Falklands and why.

ii What would be your reaction if France claimed the Channel Islands or the Isle of Wight? If France invaded, what do you think would be the consequence of a war between the two countries, and what do you think would be its outcome?

iii Work in a small group. Imagine that you are a doctor's family living on either the Isle of Wight or one of the Channel Islands. You hear on the news that you have been invaded by the French who are claiming your island. How do you react? What do you decide to do? Does every member of the family feel the same? Perhaps your son or daughter already has a French girl or boyfriend. How does this affect their reaction?

A neighbour arrives and tells you that a badly wounded French soldier is at their house and needs the doctor's help. What does the family do?

iv How do you think the Falklands problem should be sorted out?

Imagine that you are at a United Nations meeting set up to resolve the question of sovereignty of the Falkland Islands once and for all. Divide the group into parties representing Britain, Argentina, the Falkland Islanders and other member nations of the United Nations. Appoint someone to preside over the proceedings in the role of the Secretary General. Allow yourselves a set time to prepare your cases and for the debate, during which the other nations can ask questions, and at the end of which, a vote should be taken as to what should happen to the Falkland Islands.

Related reading
There are now a large number of books available on the subject of the war. This is just a small selection:

The Winter War, by Patrick Bishop and John Witherow (Quartet).
The Battle for the Falklands, by Max Hastings and Simon Jenkins (Michael Joseph).
The Falklands War, by the Sunday Times Insight Team (Andre Deutsch).
Prison Diary, Argentina, by Simon Winchester (Andre Deutsch). An unusual perspective, by one of three British journalists imprisoned in Argentina throughout the conflict.
Our Falklands War, by Geoffrey Underwood (Maritime Books).
A Message from the Falklands, compiled by Hugh Tinker — the letters of David Tinker, RN (Junction Books).
The Falklands War, A Visual Diary, by Linda Kitson — the official British war artist (Mitchell Beazley).

RUMOUR, PROPAGANDA, TRUTH AND CENSORSHIP

We've got to kill him Sarah. We've got to do our
bit. . . . And if you don't agree it's our duty, you're not a
patriot. You're a traitor.

MICHAEL

Patriotism is the last refuge of a scoundrel.

DR JOHNSON

Rumours abound in wartime — and some of them turn out to
have been deliberately invented to further military ends.
   Many Argentinian soldiers believed that the Gurkhas
killed their own wounded, went into battle crazed on drugs,
and even that they ate their prisoners. Similar stories of
cannibalism were rife about the Germans in both World
Wars. A rumour was also circulated amongst the Argentinians that British special forces had infiltrated their ranks,
dressed in Argentinian uniform and speaking perfect
Spanish. One soldier is reported to have said that 'There was
so much fear we tried to find questions to ask them that an
Argentinian would know easily, but that an English
commando would not know, even if he spoke perfect Spanish.'
On the British side, the superb skill and great courage of the
Argentinian bomber pilots soon led to rumours that they were
suicide pilots, i.e. demented rather than courageous.
   Ministry of Defence officials told journalists covering the
campaign that hunger had forced Argentinian soldiers to eat
cats and dogs and that they were suffering from dysentery.
Whilst there were supply problems with the troops in

outlying areas of the Falklands, these, and other stories from less-official sources, were obviously intended to boost the morale of the British troops and their relations at home, by presenting a picture of a demoralised enemy. Naturally enough, similar tales of the barbarity of the invaders and the bravery of the resistance abounded amongst the civilian population.

In Britain, a war of words of a different sort broke out over coverage of the conflict by the news media. The BBC, in particular was subjected to attack. On May 11, 1982, the managing director of BBC Radio, Mr Richard Francis, defended their coverage. He said:

'The BBC has no role to boost the morale of British troops or rally the British people round the flag. Our job is not jingo, it is to provide the most reliable account of confusing and worrying events.

'To suppress Argentine pictures for fear of appearing unpatriotic would be ignoble at the least. The widow of Portsmouth is no different from the widow of Buenos Aires. The BBC needs no lesson in patriotism. Truth is the best propaganda.'

On May 7, *The Sun* accused the 'pygmy' *Guardian*, the 'whining, timorous' *Daily Mirror*, and the BBC's Peter Snow of treason — a statement that the National Union of Journalists immediately described as 'odious and hysterical'. The editor of *The Guardian* said the attack was 'Sad and despicable — but I am not surprised'. The Mirror later did a huge front page piece about its rival, headlined 'The Harlot of Fleet Street'.

In Argentina in early May, a magazine pictured Mrs Thatcher on its front page as a pirate, complete with an eye-patch. She was described as being 'guilty, an assassin and a pirate'. Argentinian radio and television, throughout the early part of the crisis, displayed slogans like 'Onward Argentina to Victory!' on its screens, with the national flag as a backdrop. Martial music was broadcast in great quantities.

We got most of our news about the crisis from the newspapers, radio and television. What do you think the role of the news media should be in such an event? Do you think that manipulation or suppression of the news is justifiable in times of national crisis?

Reporters hit at ministry's false Falkland stories

By Richard Norton-Taylor

Ministry of Defence officials told journalists covering the Falklands campaign that Argentine soldiers were eating cats and dogs, and were suffering from dysentry, though these assertions later turned out to be completely untrue, the Commons all-party defence committee was told yesterday.

Mr Robert McGowen, a Daily Express reporter, also told MPs that journalists were told that casualties after the Argentine bombing attack at Bluff Cove were minimal when in fact 50 lives had been lost, as the BBC's World Service stated in a broadcast seven hours later.

In addition to trying to mislead the media, Ministry public relations officers were sharply attacked by Mr McGowen, Mr Gareth Parry, of the Guardian, and Mr Max Hastings, of the London Standard, for an erratic, nitpicking and obstructionist attitude to the Press. Journalists on the Canberra said they were fully briefed about what to expect, but those on the Invincible received no briefing at all.

While Ministry officials blocked reports, that had already been passed by military censors in the field, the journalists said they were astonished by some of the reports that were passed by the Ministry in London. They were surprised, in particular, about references to how Argentine forces were incorrectly fusing their bombs. The Argentinians quickly got the message, Mr Parry said.

In his evidence, Mr Hastings said that the British media, apparently encouraged to speculate, "seem to have shown very little capacity for self-censorship" — a view described by Mr Chris Patten, a Conservative member of the committee, as paradoxical, given that Mr Hastings got more stories out of the Falklands than other journalists with the task force.

The committee is not expected to complete its inquiry into the Ministry's handling of information during the Falklands conflict until the end of the year. But it is clear already that the inconsistencies in censoring and the frustrations of the media were due mainly to the lack of respect towards civilian public relations officials by both journalists and the military.

The confusion and inconsistency was compounded by rivalry between the Army and the Navy and between different brigades and even between different paratroop battalions. At one stage, the SAS gave special facilities to Mr Hastings to allow him to file a story to their Hereford HQ about their activities.

The SAS felt that the more conscious the Argentinians were made of how serious their predicament was, the better, Mr Hastings said. But the story was held up by the Ministry of Defence in London for three days.

Some representatives of the media, including senior BBC executives, have suggested in their evidence that they were concerned more about the inefficiency of the vetting system rather than the principle of censorship.

The Guardian 29 July 1982

LIES!

But at least they fooled the enemy

By MARK DOWDNEY

THE Government told lies to the Press during the Falkland campaign, a Commons committee reported yesterday.

The truth was concealed and wrong information was issued for "sound military reasons," the Select Committee on Defence said.

But the danger now is that "these tactics will present risks to future credibility."

The report says that lies which misled the enemy were totally justified. But it is critical of the way the Defence Ministry treated reporters during the conflict.

Wrong

Reporting on difficulties between commanders and journalists, the MPs said that Press criticism of the lack of off-the-record briefings was "substantially vindicated."

It led to "Press and television speculation which clearly went too far."

The decision to keep all briefings formal and on the record was made by Defence Secretary John Nott on the advice of the Defence Ministry's spokesman Ian McDonald.

The advice was wrong, the report says. In future, it goes on, "the Defence Secretary should appoint one of his Ministers to take day-to-day responsibility for defence information policy."

But the Minister, it seems, need not tell the whole truth. The report goes on to say that future British Governments should not rely on "the sense of fairness and objectivity of the world's media" but should appreciate the importance of propaganda.

Channelling information through one Minister would also avoid "the lack of co-operation and trust between the Services and their public relations departments" which was a feature of the Falklands conflict.

Goals

The MPs say that the Government was "generally successful in the information war," and that "the basic goals of information policy during wartime were met and the credibility of British government spokesmen was maintained."

And they conclude that "as a result of our inquiry, some of the more obvious shortcomings both of the Ministry and the media will be avoided in future."

Daily Mirror 17 December 1982

Even in more normal times it is interesting to look at the way different newspapers, and different television news programmes, handle the same events. Look at the way several papers treat the same story, and see if you can arrive at a common core of 'truth' from the various accounts, or identify the political attitude of the various organs.

Look at:

● Where the story is in the newspaper.
● Whether there is a picture.
● What the caption is.
● What hard facts are included in the story.
● Who the newspapers quote as authorities, and what their attitude is to them.
● Whether the newspapers approve or disapprove of the event and/or the people involved. How can you tell?

i   Take an incident that you have recently witnessed and write it up as a newspaper story — first from one point of view, and then from an opposite position.

ii   **Or** working in small groups, take an incident that you have seen or invent one — perhaps an accident or a theft — and recreate it for other groups in the class. Then ask them to describe it in detail, or in turn recreate the event. You could do this like an acted-out game of Chinese Whispers with each group or individual acting the incident for the next one that hasn't seen it and see how close the final acted incident is to the original.

iii   Imagine that you are on the Falkland Islands at the time of the events happening in *A Game of Soldiers*. The newspapers have got hold of some details of how the young conscript died. Work with a partner. One of you is a reporter and the other is one of the children in the play. What kinds of questions will the reporter ask in order to get a good story? What kinds of details will the reporter be interested in?

Now reverse roles. The other person is now the reporter and their partner is one of the parents of the children in the play. Again, think of the facts which the reporter will want to establish.

Write a newspaper story from these interviews. Will the newspaper want to emphasise any particular angle on the story? Will any of the facts be altered or distorted?

iv   If the reporters heard rumours that farmers had been killing Argentinian conscripts, how would they go about establishing the facts? Work in small groups and set your scene in a pub on the Falklands. The pub is full of local farmers and a reporter has come to try to find out if there is any truth in the rumours that are circulating. What can the reporter discover, and how will the story be written up for the newspapers?

Related reading
Bad News, by the Glasgow University Media Group
    (Routledge and Kegan Paul).
Gotcha. The Media, the Government and the Falklands Crisis,
    by Robert Harris (Faber and Faber).

THE ROLE OF MEN AND WOMEN IN WAR

It has been said that men are the aggressive sex, who start wars, and women the nurses, mothers and wives who deal with its aftermath. Even in *A Game of Soldiers* there is a definite difference in attitude between Michael and Sarah. The following quotes and extracts may help you explore the topic.

To a certain extent a boy's upbringing is centred on warlike activities and war stories.

DAVID TINKER, RN

And gentlemen in England now abed
Shall think themselves accursed they were not here,
And hold their manhoods cheap whiles any speaks
That fought with us upon St Crispin's Day.

SHAKESPEARE, *Henry V*

There they go marching all in step so gay!
Smooth-cheeked and golden, food for shells and guns.
Blithely they go as to a wedding day,
The Mothers' sons.

KATHARINE TYNAN, 1914

i   In some countries, women are conscripted into the fighting forces. Imagine that the conscript in *A Game of Soldiers* is a 17-year-old girl. Write or improvise a scene in which the children make this discovery. How do you think their various attitudes would have been affected.

64

ii   Look at the pages made up from a girls' comic, 'Tammy', and a boys' comic, 'Battle Action Force' on pages 66-69. What is most noticeable about each? And how typical are they of boys' and girls' comics?

iii   Taking some of these comic strip pictures, build a story around them and either draw or act out the story, keeping the cartoon style.

iv   Tell the story of *A Game of Soldiers* in comic strip style, either by improvising it or drawing it. An 'artist' and a 'bubble writer' could work together on this.

v   Make lists to show what people think of as typical boys' games and typical girls' games, and typical boys' toys and typical girls' toys. What do they tell you about the way boys and girls grow up? Do you think this could be, or should be changed?

vi   Imagine that you are a member of the opposite sex and write a diary of the day that you hear your country has been declared at war with another.

vii   If you are a boy, imagine that you are the mother or girlfriend of a boy who has just been conscripted to fight in your country's war. Write a letter to a friend in which you describe your reaction to the news and the boy's leavetaking.

viii   If you are a girl, imagine that you are a boy who has just been conscripted to fight, and write a letter to a friend describing your own reaction and that of your mother or girlfriend to the news and to your departure.

xi   There have been quite a few women in the past who have disguised themselves as soldiers and fought alongside men. For example, Christian Davies, who originally joined the dragoons at the end of the seventeenth century to find her husband, but stayed and fought with them for nearly twenty years. There were also women fighting in Nelson's navy, and women pirates. Write, or draw a comic strip about a woman disguised as a man in either the Civil War of the mid 17th

century, or the war against the Japanese. **Or**, in a small group, improvise the story of a woman who decides to go to war as a soldier. Why does the girl decide to go: because she wants to fight for her country; to find her boyfriend or brother; to have an adventure? How would she behave in order to convince the men that she is a man? How might she be discovered and what would happen to her?

CHILDREN AND WAR

I'm fed up with this war. It's spoiled everything.
Nothing's any fun no more. It's ruinated.

THOMAS

I'm tired and sick of war. Its glory is all moonshine. War
is hell.

GENERAL SHERMAN, 1879

i Imagine that, like the children in the play, you also lived
in the Falklands during the war, but in an area which was
captured by Argentinian troops. A young conscript has been
posted outside your home. Explore what might happen if you
tried to talk to the soldier. What can you find out about
conditions in the army, and about his feelings and attitudes?

ii Your parents are away when your home comes under
heavy bombardment. What action will you take to make
yourselves as safe as possible? Improvise a scene which shows
how you and the other members of your family survived the
air raid.

iii Soldiers are posted all round your village. You have a
very important reason for wanting to get out of the village.
How will you leave without being seen? If anyone challenges
you, can you give a convincing explanation of what you are
doing and where you are going? Will you be allowed through?

iv Imagine that all the children who live in your area are to
be evacuated — moved to a place of safety for the duration of

the conflict. You are to be sent to distant relations who live a long way away and whom you do not really know. Explore what happens when you arrive at your new home. How do you fit in with this new family? Are your ideas and ways of doing things different? Improvise a scene which reveals the difficulties of living with strangers through the tensions and worries of wartime. Write a letter to your parents describing what life is like for you now, or, as one of the adults in charge, write to the parents of the children you are looking after. Is their behaviour all that you could wish for?

Related reading

WORLD WARS

Carrie's War, by Nina Bawden (Puffin).
Tom Fobble's Day, by Alan Garner (Fontana Lions)
I Am David, by Anne Helm (Puffin).
Goodnight Mr Tom, Michelle Magorian (Puffin).
War Horse, by Michael Morpurgo (Collins Cascades).
The Evacuees, by Jack Rosenthal (play) (Penguin).
The Silver Sword, by Ian Serraillier (Puffin).
When the Siren Wailed, by Noel Streatfield (Puffin).
The Dolphin Country, by Jill Paton Walsh (Puffin).
Fireweed, by Jill Paton Walsh (Puffin).
Summer of the Zeppelin, by Elsie McCutcheon (Collins Cascades).

NORTHERN IRELAND (although not officially a war, probably the nearest most British children come to the experience)

The Deserter, by Nigel Grey (Fontana Lions).
The Twelfth Day of July, by Joan Lingard (Puffin).
Across the Barricades, by Joan Lingard (Puffin).

ANTHOLOGIES

Up the Line to Death, by Brian Gardner — a selection of First World War poetry (Methuen).
Scars Upon my Heart, by Catherine Reilly — a selection of women's poetry from the First World War (Virago).
Voices from the Great War, by Peter Vansittart — an anthology of poetry, speeches, letters, songs, etc (Penguin).